Lasers:
Theory and Practice

LASERS: THEORY AND PRACTICE

Dirk R. Baur

Elektor Electronics (Publishing)

Elektor Electronics (Publishing)
P.O. Box 1414
Dorchester
England DT2 8YH

British Library Cataloguing in Publication Data
A catalogue record for this book is available from the British Library

ISBN 0 905705 52 1

Translation and make-up: R.J. Hardy, M.Sc.

First published in the United Kingdom 1997

© Segment BV 1996

Printed in the Netherlands by Giethoorn-NND, Meppel

Contents

Other books from Elektor Electronics

1. Introduction

Since we can no longer imagine a world without lasers, this book was written to give the reader a basic idea – and hands-on experience – of the many functions and applications of lasers. Their presence is evident not just at industrial fairs and exhibitions: a look at any of the professional physics/electronics/medical magazines and journals shows that lasers play a major role in many disciplines.

Low-power lasers are generally of the diode or semiconductor type. These are small, light, very robust, insensitive to interference, but produce only relatively low powers. One of their best known applications is in CD players. The first of these players used HeNe (helium-neon) lasers, but modern ones use infra-red diodes almost exclusively. These lasers have made possible the enormous price reductions in CD players since the early 1990s.

Although the price of helium-neon (HeNe) lasers has also come down, these lasers are now found primarily in electronic maintenance equipment. Many readers may remember the first of these affordable versions in their shiny aluminium housing becoming obtainable from mail-order firms: they are still available.

Helium-neon lasers, developed and first produced in the 1980s, were technically very advanced pieces of equipment, originally intended for use in laser-disc players. Now, mainly because the normal life of an He-Ne laser is about ten years, many of these shiny units bought then are reaching the end of their useful life. Nevertheless, they led the way to today's inexpensive consumer lasers.

Over the past few years, light-emitting diodes (LEDs) have come into use for many applications. Many people may not know that these diodes, used in low-cost laser-pens, were developed for CD players. Because of the enormous demand, light-emitting diodes have become much cheaper. For example, over the past five years, the price of a laser-pen has dropped by almost 80 per cent. In the same period, the price of a CD player has also dropped dramatically.

Today, lasers are used in architecture to measure walls, lamp posts, doors, tunnels, shafts, and even whole buildings; in automobile engineering to measure all sorts of part; and in high-precision spirit levels, to name but a few. Walls are erected with unprecedented precision: traditional geodelites are becoming obsolescent. Lasers are also used in crime fighting; for instance, in high-precision speed traps to catch the unwary, speeding motorist. These are but a few examples of the many applications of lasers that are deemed of interest to readers of this book.

Although the laser is a relatively new device (the first practical one was built in 1960 by the American physicist Theodore Maiman on the basis of theoretical work by Charles Townes and Arthur Schawlow), many improvements and a number of new types have already come about in its short life. When Maiman showed an astonished audience his brainchild, which was then only known from science fiction, even he did not realize what an effect it would have on the industrial world. His ruby laser, which was only the size of a man's fist, emitted high-energy, short-duration pulses and paved the way for new, progressive and powerful laser equipment. As in the case of computers, the price of lasers has plummeted. Today, most lasers are inexpensive, often of the throw-away type, and used in countless industrial equipment and consumer products. What is not generally known is that many lasers are readily available at very reasonable prices to amateur constructors and designers. Small second-hand laser tubes may be obtained at very low prices. The way is therefore clear for lasers to be utilized by a much wider circle of constructors. All that is needed is a small laser tube, some miscellaneous components and … this book.

At what readership is this book aimed?
The book is aimed at a wide range of interested readers. If you are a beginner in electronics, you will undoubtedly enjoy the many circuits and construction proposals it contains. But the advanced constructor will also find satisfaction in the countless practical tips as well as the expandable home construction projects such as the highly sensitive laser seismograph. Of course, a book such as this cannot possibly cover all the many possibilities offered by laser technology. The author has confined himself to what he feels are the most interesting topics for as wide a readership as possible.

Safety first!

Any laser, even the smallest, forms a danger for the human eye. In laser technology there is one rule that must be obeyed at all times: Never, ever look into a laser beam or even into its reflection! In this context, it should be borne in mind that even a 1 mW laser is about 1000 times as bright as summer sunlight. Before you start any work on a laser project, take off any rings, watches, bracelets and other shiny personal ornament that may reflect the laser beam. Also, make sure at all times that there is nobody else in the path of the beam. Children are particularly curious and will want to find out what happens in the beam.

Apart from the laser beam, the high voltages in the power supply may be lethal. For instance, the high tension at the terminals of a 5 mW He-Ne laser at the instant it is triggered is about 10,000 V. True the current is small but, nevertheless, such a high voltage must be treated with respect. So, before touching any part of the power supply or removing the connections to the laser tube, short-circuit the storage capacitors by linking the anode to the cathode. Better safe than sorry!

2. Fundamentals

The first laser was constructed in 1960 and it might be thought that it was first conceived about two or three years earlier. This is, however, not so. It is fairly certain that the man who first thought of the possibility of a laser was none other than Albert Einstein (1879–1955).

Einstein was a theoretical physicist and a towering genius. But, as so many theoretical physicists, he left the practical application of his pioneering ideas to others. The first inkling of _Light Amplification by Stimulated Emission of Radiation_ was a by-product of Einstein's best-known works, the Special Theory of Relativity (1905) and the General Theory of Relativity (1915). Einstein formulated that light is a stream of particles, called photons, which are moving as a uniform wave. He was sure that it must be possible to focus such a stream of photons into a narrow beam, which would consequently be coherent. More important was the subsequent assumption that a large amount of energy could be concentrated in such a beam. He did not suggest how this was to be achieved – that was not his problem.

Until Einstein's prediction, it was believed that a photon could interact with an atom in only two ways: it could be absorbed and raise the atom to a higher energy level or be emitted as the atom dropped to a lower energy level. This is called spontaneous emission. It was Einstein's insight to propose a third possibility: that a photon with energy corresponding to that of an energy-level transition could stimulate an atom in the upper level to drop to the lower level, in the process stimulating the emission of another photon with the same energy as the first. He then concluded that the second photon in turn would stimulate an atom in the upper level to drop to the lower level, and so on, so that a chain reaction would be set up. This process would continue until the primary energy source is disabled.

The raising of an atom to a higher level is called excitation (sometimes pumping). Atoms may be excited in various ways, for instance, by electricity and heat. There are, of course, other kinds of energy. For instance, light from a krypton lamp, a xenon flash tube, or a laser may be used. The neon atoms in a neon tube are raised to a higher energy level with the aid of a very high voltage, which is applied to the tube via two electrodes. The gas in the tube then starts to emit photons. When the electrical charge is high enough, the majority of the atoms are excited whereupon the tube lights. When there are more high-level than low-level atoms available, a so-called population inversion occurs. This is an essential process in the operation of a laser. The photons released in a neon tube are totally random and decay by emitting light. If, however, a mirror is placed at either end of the tube, many photons can return to the tube and oscillate between the two mirrors. Every time it transverses the tube it collides with one or more atoms. When many of these atoms are in the excited state, they emit a photon that has the same characteristics as the colliding photon: same polarity and phase, wavelength – an identical twin, as it were. This process is called simply light amplification.

In theory, when both mirrors reflect totally and are exactly in line with one another, the photons will continue to travel from one to the other and never leave the tube. This will then overheat and explode since the light energy cannot be released. When the mirror at one end is moved some distance away from the tube, some of the photons can escape in the form of a beam of amplified light. However, since the mirror allows only some of the photons to escape, the others remain in the tube and return to the other mirror so that the chain reaction remains enabled. This process results in a continuous light wave, normally abbreviated to cw.

2.1. History of the laser

1916 – Einstein formulates the theoretical possibility of stimulated emission of light.
1954 – The first microwave laser (normally called maser) is designed.
1960 – The first optical laser is designed.
1961 – The first HeNe laser is designed.
1962 – The first semiconductor laser is designed.
1964 – The argon laser is developed by William Bridges, working at the Hughes Aircraft Corporation.
1965 – Microwave laser radiation is discovered in the Orion Nebula.
1970 – Laser action in stars is given consideration.
1973 – Laser radiation is discovered in quasars.
1984 – The first X-ray laser is designed.

There are few other important dates in the development of the laser. It is interesting to note that L. Schawlow, one of the early pioneers of laser technology, once said: "When we got the first laser to function, I and my colleagues were surprised how easy it was. At the beginning of our research and development, we all thought that it would be rather complicated. However, once you know how it works, it really is very simple. All that we lacked in the early stages were ideas and conceptions."

...and there was (laser) light
Although we have used a neon tube to show how laser light is generated by the activity of atoms and photons, it must be said that neon gas is not as efficient as other materials. Other materials on which lasers can be based may be be solid, liquid or gas. The first optical laser, designed in 1960 by Theodore Maiman, a young physicist working at the Hughes Research Laboratories in Malibu, California, used a synthetic ruby crystal, although some theorists said that such a crystal would not work. The world's first practical laser consisted of a rod of synthetic ruby with reflecting coatings at both ends and surrounded by a helical flashlamp (Figure 2-1).

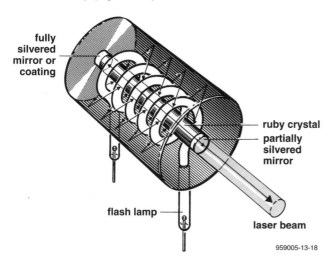

fully silvered mirror or coating

ruby crystal
partially silvered mirror

flash lamp

laser beam

959005-13-18

*Figure 2-1
The world's first
optical laser*

When the lamp is pulsed, concentrated light falls on to the ruby crystal, whereupon the laser action commences in the same way as described for the neon tube. The white light of the flashlamp falls on to the atoms of the ruby crystal. This absorbs the green and blue spectra, which raises the energy level of the atoms. After a few milliseconds, they return to the lower energy level and then, after another few milliseconds to the higher energy level. In this way photons are released (Figure 2-2). The photons oscillate between the two reflecting coating and amplify the emission. At a given instant a pulse of red light emerges from one end of the rod which has a partially transparent coating.

The ruby laser remains in commercial use, although its popularity has declined in recent years.

Figure 2-2.
Schematic showing
how photons are
released

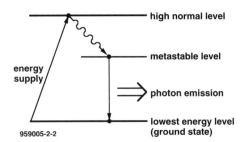

Within a short time after Maiman's demonstration of the ruby laser, a number of other types of laser were reported. The first solid-state laser, using trivalent uranium ions in calcium fluoride, designed by Sorokin and Stevenson in late 1960, has never been put into practical use. In 1961, however, appeared the first helium-neon laser, designed by Javan, Bennett, and Herriott at the Bell Telephone Laboratories in New Jersey. Later that year, Johnson and Nassau demonstrated another solid-state laser, based on calcium tungstate doped with neodymium ($CaWO4$).

In 1962, the first semiconductor diode laser was developed almost simultaneously by three independent organizations: the General Electric Research Laboratories in Schenectady, New York; the IBM Watson Research Center in Yorktown Heights, New York; and MIT's Lincoln Laboratories in Lexington, Massachuchetts. All three had used gallium arsenide diodes cooled in liquid nitrogen and pulsed with high-current pulses of a few microseconds duration.

2.2 Classification of lasers

As mentioned earlier, lasers may be based on a solid, a liquid or a gas. Most types fall into one of the following categories:

crystal;
glass;

gas;
excimer;
chemical;
semiconductor;
liquid.
We shall have a closer look at all these types.

Crystal and glass

Crystal and glass lasers are solid-state lasers*. The synthetic ruby used by Maiman is made from aluminium oxide doped with a small number of chromium atoms. The reason that synthetic rather than natural ruby is used is that the synthetic type is much purer. Without this purity laser action would be impossible.

One of today's best selling solid-state lasers is the neodymium yttrium aluminium garnet (Nd:YAG) type, first demonstrated by Geusic, Marcos and Uitert in 1964. Similar to the ruby laser, a rod of Nd:YAG is the actual generator of the laser beam. It is pumped optically and produces light in the infra-red region (about 1060 nm). An Nd:YAG laser can operate in the continuous-wave mode, since Nd:YAG is an excellent heat conductor in contrast to the ruby laser which, owing to its poor heat conduction, can only work in the pulsed mode.

Neodymium may also be mixed with glass to form an Nd:glass laser. This has the great advantage of being inexpensive, but it suffers from the poor heat conduction of glass, so that it can be used in the pulsed mode only.

The power of a diode-pumped Nd:YAG laser varies from about five watts to several hundred watts in continuous-wave mode. If a Kerr cell or a chopper is inserted between the resonators, the reflectivity or Q of the resonator is made small while the population inversion is built up to its peak value. The Q is then increased to a high value, whereupon an intense burst of energy almost completely empties the high energy states in about 10^{-8} seconds. In this way, powers of up to a megawatt can be generated. The highest possible pulse power is obtained when the pulse-pause period is made equal to the saturation time

---

* The reader should note that in laser technology the word *solid-state* has a different meaning from that in electronics: it signifies an active medium consisting of a non-conductive solid, a crystalline material, or doped glass. Semiconductor lasers are considered functionally different types, although they are made of solids, because of fundamental differences in operation.

of the crystal.

Gas lasers

Gas lasers come in many varieties (more than 5000 possible ones are known, but only a few dozen are in practical use) and head the list of commercially available types. Their popularity arises from the ease with which they can be built and tested. The most frequently used gases are:

helium-neon;
helium-cadmium;
argon;
krypton;
carbon dioxide.

Figure 2-3 Helium-neon (He-Ne) laser

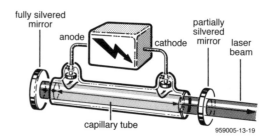

The helium-neon (He-Ne) laser (Figure 2-3) is more frequently used than any other type of gas laser. It is a straighforward, air-cooled model that provides output powers from 0.1 mW up to 200 mW in laboratory types that may be several metres (up to10 ft) long. Second-hand He-Ne tubes are available at fairly low prices. They require a high supply voltage but do not draw much current. Their efficiency, depending on the application, lies between 0.02 per cent and 0.05 per cent. A typical He-Ne tube is shown in Figure 2-4.

Figure 2-4 Helium-neon tube (1 mW)

Multi-line He-Ne lasers that emit light of various colours are a new development. The emitted light is analysed into a frequency spectrum with the aid of a grating. The wanted colour may be obtained with the use of a spectral filter. Note, however, that the output power is highest at the standard wavelength of 632.8 nm; at other wavelengths it is lower.

The carbon-dioxide (CO_2) laser is one of the most versatile and most powerful gas types on the market. It emits infra-red radiation between 900 nm and 1100 nm and may operate in cw or pulsed mode. Owing to the (relatively) long wavelength it is not really suitable for all materials. Although its efficiency may be greater than 10 per cent, a CO_2 laser must be water-cooled since, owing to its small dimensions and a power dissipation of about 90 per cent, overheating may occur. Even the resonator mirrors may be water-cooled. Small CO_2 tubes with power outputs of up to 5 watts are readily available at reasonable cost. The most expensive part is, as with many types of laser, the power supply. Compared with He-Ne lasers, CO_2 lasers draw a much smaller current, but need an appreciably higher supply voltage.

Argon and krypton lasers are today the most frequently used types in the show business and holography. These lasers have several worthwhile properties, among which that of the simultaneous generation of laser beams at several wavelengths spread over the entire colour spectrum. An argon laser produces from the ultraviolet (334 nm) up the bright green (528.7 nm) and many other colours in between. The highest outputs occur at 488 nm and at 514.5 nm. A krypton laser emits from red to well into the infra-red range at 800 nm.

The white-light krypton laser work is, in fact, not a krypton laser at all. Its active medium is a mixture of argon and krypton, which emits wavelengths from 454 nm up to 800 nm. Depending on the ratio between the two gases and the optics, that is, the mirrors, used, white light is emitted. Different mirrors give totally different outputs. Therefore, distinct mirrors are used to obtain the desired colour. To enhance the efficiency, the mirrors are given multiple coatings; a first-class mirror may have as many as 100 coatings. The cost of such mirrors is very high and normally beyond most individuals' means. Moreover, the efficiency of a laser so equipped is not very good: a modern mixed-gas laser with an input of 10 kW may have an output of only 5 watts – an efficiency of 0.05 per cent. An argon laser is rather better with an efficiency of 0.1 per cent. These lasers are, of course, water-cooled, although smaller models may be air-cooled.

There are ways and means to improve the power output, that is, the efficiency, of a laser. One of these makes use of the magnetic field around the laser beam generator. This field helps in keeping the photons within the medium so that

959005-13-59

even more atoms may be excited. Each inert gas reacts differently; krypton, for instance, attenuates the red emission when the magnetic field is increased, whereas argon attenuates the blue light. Because of this behaviour, the colour of light emitted by a mixed-gas laser can be changed by altering the strength of the magnetic field. The emission of an He-Ne laser may be amplified up to a point, after which any increase in the magnetic field has no effect on the emitted light.

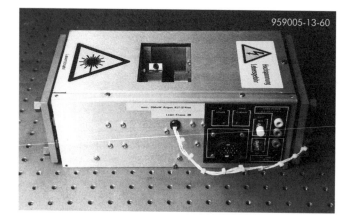

959005-13-60

Other external means to increase the power output are virtually non-existent. Some time ago, Spectra Physics, an American company, brought out a replacement laser tube called 'Color Shot' which, to all appearances, was identical to the original model but had three times the power output for the same power input. This was made possible by the following process. The more gas is contained in the actual discharge path and between the resonator mirrors, the more power can be generated. This may be achieved by making the resonator longer: the longer this is, the higher the output. It is, of course, also possible to increase the diameter of the tube. This has a draw-back, however, because when the tube diameter is increased, the diameter and divergence of the beam are also larger. There is a solution to this and that is to use a focusing mirror, which enables a clean, narrow beam to be obtained. This reduces the service-friendliness of the laser, however, since the actual point of emission is narrower than that obtained by traditional optics. Moreover, the beam divergence becomes greater. All in all, such means must be seen as a compromise.

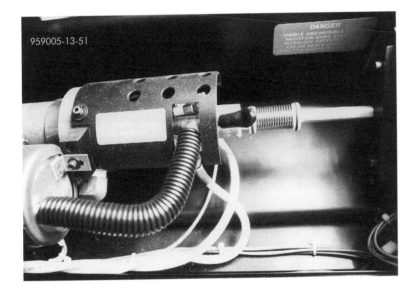

Figure 2-7.
Part of a coherent
Innova tube
(Brewster window with
cover)

Excimer lasers

The term excimer laser does not refere to a single device, but to a family of lasers with similar output characteristics. All emit powerful pulses lasting nanoseconds at wavelengths near the ultraviolet region.

The name excimer is a contraction of 'excited dimer', that is a molecule formed by two identical atoms that exists only in an excited state, for instance, He_2 and Xe_2. Today, it is used in a broader meaning for any diatomic molecule in which the component atoms are bound in the excited state, but not in the ground state.

Inert gases like argon, krypton and xenon react electrically with halogens like chlorine, fluorine, iodine or bromine to form an excimer. When the excimer emits a photon, it does not return to its ground, but to its original diatomic form.

The most interesting aspect of an excimer laser is its strong, high-energy, ultraviolet emission in the range 193–351 nm. The short wavelengths facilitate the manufacture of integrated circuits and transistors.

Chemical lasers

Chemical lasers have found particular attraction by military agencies because of their potential to generate high powers. In these lasers, a chemical reaction excites and atom or molecule to the upper laser level. Most of these lasers operate on infra-red vibrational transitions of diatomic molecules, particularly hydrogen halides. They are ignited by a trigger circuit or open flame. It stands to reason that such a laser can be used only once, but in that one operation it releases an enormous amount of energy. The amount of energy is so large that the laser mirrors melt or vaporize. These lasers will be reverted to later (laser weapons).

Semiconductor lasers

Semiconductor lasers are undoubtedly the most common types. They outsell all other types of laser by a factor of 100 or more. Since the first of this type of laser appeared in 1962, their rate of development has accelerated enormously because of their application in such popular fields as fibre-optic communica-

Figure 2-8
Laser pens

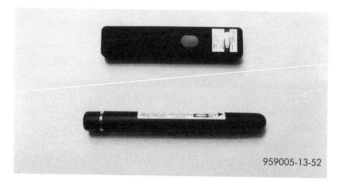

959005-13-52

tions, compact-disk players and laser printers.

There are various kinds of semiconductor laser; all are excited when, at low current densities, current carriers recombine at the p-n junction of a semiconductor such as a diode. This happens when current is flowing through a forward-biased diode. The recombination causes the spontaneous emission of light, so that the semiconductor acts as an incoherent light-emitting diode (LED). When the current density is high, and if the diode includes reflective facets, the semiconductor can operate as a laser.

Although there are different kinds of laser diode, they all consist fundamentally of a block of semiconductor (usually GaAs or InP) in which part is doped with electron donors to form n-type material and the other part is doped with electron acceptors to form p-type material – very much like a standard LED. However, laser diodes have internal structures that make their output more directional than the spontaneous emission from an LED. The end facets are coated or polished to reflect incident light. As in all lasers, initial spontaneous emission is reflected back and forth between the cavity mirror.

A diode laser produces stimulated emission only if the voltage applied to the diode exceeds the potential barrier; depending on the type of diode, this voltage should be 1.8–3 V. If no or insufficient voltage is applied, because of ambient heat only a few electrons pass from the n-material to the p-material. When the voltage exceeds the potential barrier, some of the electrons speed up and fast ones will collide with slower ones and raise them to a higher level. Some of these emit a photon and the laser action is initiated.

Since the emission, as in the case of an LED, is radiated at a fairly large angle, it must be passed through a collimator with short focal distance. Since the aperture of most laser diodes is rectangular, the output beam is initially also rectangular and only becomes circular a few centimetres away from the diode.

Liquid lasers

For all practical purposes, the only liquid laser is the tunable dye laser, in which the active medium is a fluorescent organic dye dissolved in liquid solvent and contained in a glass tube. The medium is normally optically pumped – often by an external CO_2 laser. Although its efficiency is rather low, its attractions – tuneable output wavelength and ability to produce very short pulses – are so important that the low efficiency is of no consequence in most applications.

2.3 Modes of operation

Laser resonators have two distinct types of mode: transverse and longitudinal. Transverse modes manifest themselves in the cross-sectional profile of the beam, that is, in its intensity pattern. Longitudinal modes correspond to different resonances along the length of the laser cavity which occur at different frequencies or wavelengths within the gain bandwidth of the laser. We shall first consider the longitudinal mode.

Anyone conversant with fundamental high-frequency electronics knows what a resonant circuit is. Such a circuit resonates only at a certain frequency, determined by the circuit elements, or a multiple thereof. The narrower the bandwidth of the circuit, the more precise must be the excitation frequency. A similar situation occurs in a laser. In an undamped, optical resonator there are relationships between elements in an axial direction similar to those in a resonant circuit. Here, too, the peak values at the resonator mirrors must be zero for excitation to take place. If this were not so, a short-circuit current would ensue in the metallic mirror and this would cause the oscillatory field to collapse. It follows that longitudinal modes come closer together when the resonator length is increased. It may happen that several modes become superimposed on each other, provided that they are compatible with the resonator dimensions.

Transverse modes are classified according to the number of nulls that appear across the beam cross-section in two directions. The lowest order, or fundamental mode, where intensity peaks at the centre, is known as TEM_{00} (Transverse Electromagnetic Mode). Transverse modes are best imagined as the cone of a drive unit (loudspeaker). A cone has a resonant frequency at which it vibrates backwards and forwards to set air in motion. If an harmonic, that is, a multiple of the resonant frequency, is applied, the cone starts vibrating in a different rhythm. There is then not only a peak at the centre of the cone, but two peaks, one at the centre and another somewhere between the centre and the edge of the cone. In other words, a multimode situation has arisen. If then the edge of the cone is tapped, a new vibration is set up on to which the earlier two are superimposed. This new vibration is not linear and is distributed irregularly across the membrane. Similar superimpositions occur on a laser beam when the cavity mirrors are convex.

A mode with a single null along one axis and no null in the perpendicular direction is classified as TEM_{01} or TEM_{10}, depending on the orientation. A sampling of these modes produced by stable resonators is given in the table in Figure 2-9. If a laser beam is dispersed through a lens, its projection on to a screen is similar to the table.

Multimode operations are undesirable in many applications, but they can often deliver more power in a poorer-quality beam. They are certainly not permissible in holography where the illumination of the object must not be disturbed. Multimode operation may be prevented by, for instance, an apertured diaphragm between resonator and medium, which filters out undesired modes.

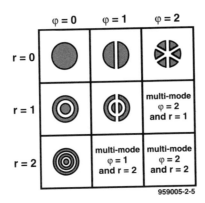

Figure 2-9
Table of lower-order modes
φ = longitudinal
r = transverse
TEM_{00} means that
φ = 0 and r = 0

This does affect the output power of the laser, however. Multimode operation should be prevented by the use of appropriate resonators, correct adjustment, and the use of homogeneous materials.

Today, mode selection is effected by an etalon – a kind of interferometer. It consists of an air film enclosed between half-silvered plane parallel plates of glass or quartz having a fixed separation. Standing waves, similar to those in the resonator, ensue in the air film; their frequency is determined by the distance between the plates and the angle at which the laser beam falls on to the etalon. Owing to the small separation of the plates, the frequency of the standing waves will be higher than the laser frequency. Normally, the etalon and laser oscillate in unison so that operation takes place in one mode only.

2.4 Wavelength and frequency

Knowing or being able to determine the wavelength or frequency of a laser is vital for all applications. After all, proper and effective operation depends on the wavelength of the emitted beam. To obtain a white beam, the laser range must be between 450 nm and 650 nm. As a reminder – see Figure 2-10 – visible light for the human eye has wavelengths between 400 nm (violet) and 740 nm (deep red). The radiation becomes infra-red above 750 nm, and ultraviolet below 400 nm. Single wavelengths, also called lines, occur in the output of an argon-krypton (mixed-gas) laser; for instance, 454 nm and 488 nm for blue light; 514 nm and 528 nm for green light; 583 nm for yellow light 605 nm and 633 nm for red light. The lines between these are not important and have low power. Since white light is composed of all wavelengths between the two limits men-

Figure 2-10
Part of the electro-
magnetic spectrum.

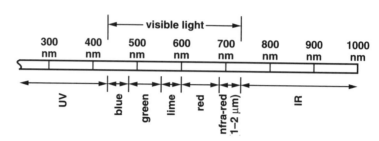

tioned earlier, a mixed-gas laser is not a true white-light laser, although it is called so.

The output of the red (632.8 nm) He-Ne laser also contains a number of different lines which can be selected with the aid of suitable resonator mirrors, for instance, 612 nm, 543 nm and 598 nm. An argon laser emits several lines between green and blue: 454 nm and 540 nm. Almost all gas lasers emit a number of lines of varying output power. The most important of these are shown in Figure 2-10.

The relationship between frequency, f, in Hertz (Hz), wavelength, λ, in metres (m), and speed of light, $c = 3 \times 10^8$ m is:

$$\lambda = c/f,$$

so that in the case of a normal He-Ne laser emitting light with a wavelength of 632.8 nm, the frequency of the light is

$$f = 3 \times 10^8 / 632.8 \times 10^{-9} \approx 474 \times 10^{12} \approx 474 \text{ THz (terahertz).}$$

Figure 2-11
Beam deflector

959005-13-58

It is vital in metal working to know the exact wavelength of the laser light. The wavelength should be as small as feasible so as to ensure that the laser light is absorbed effectively by shiny metals. It is, for instance, a tedious task to cut copper with a CO_2 laser, because this material reflects most of the long-wavelength light (10.6 μm) of this type of laser. This is the reason that copper mirrors are often used to invert a laser beam. Copper must therefore be cut with laser light of a higher frequency and today this is normally provided by an Nd:YAG laser whose light has a wavelength of 1.06 μm.

2.5 Blanking of a laser beam

Blanking of a laser beam is a vital requirement in many industrial applications, be it for safety reasons (or regulations) or for measuring intervals of time. Blanking may be controlled or purely incidental. For instance, in metal working with the aid of a laser, the boundaries of an area around the laser beam are scanned (often by a light barrier). If an unwanted object enters the area, either the laser is switched off in a fraction of a second or the laser beam is blocked instantly. In its simplest form, this is done by an electromagnet that places a shutter in the path of the beam. This arrangement ensures that in case of a cable fracture or power failure the beam is blanked instantly. When the voltage returns or the cable has been repaired, the electromagnet removes the shutter so that the laser beam is available again. Note that although the method is basically

959005-photo-2

Figure 2-12
The red emergency button is shown at the top right.

Figure 2-13
Blanking of a laser
beam by a mechani-
cally operated fork

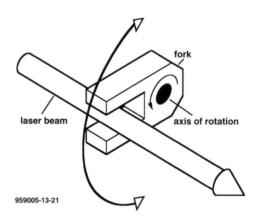

simple, it becomes more and more complicated the higher the power of the beam that has to be blanked.

An even simpler method of blanking a laser beam is to shut off its current, although this cannot be done with all lasers. In case of an emergency it is the most effective way. Almost all lasers have a sub-circuit in their power supply which can be accessed from outside (Figure 2-12) to enable the supply to the laser to be switched off. The switch to operate the circuit is fitted with a red knob which must be accessible to anybody. When this emergency switch is pressed, the laser is switched off instantly; when the emergency is over, the laser must be retriggered.

Figure 2-14
Blanking a laser
beam with a
mirror

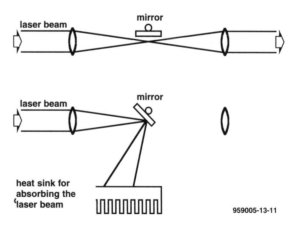

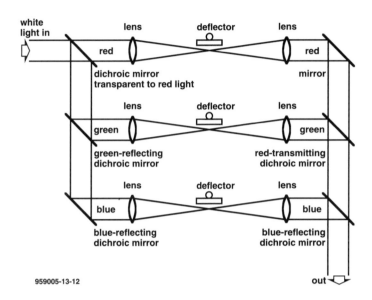

Figure 2-15
Dated mechanical
RGB colour
blending

959005-13-12

Another effective means of blanking is blocking the beam between the res-onators. A metal or synthetic shutter may be used, since there is no power involved in the operation. This is so because exactly at the instant the shutter is placed between the resonators the laser effect stops since the reflection from the mir-ror is interrupted. So, this is a power-free and simple means of blocking the beam.

A so-called Q switch may be used instead of a mechanical means of releas-ing the shutter. In this arrangement, the laser may be switched on and off in the megahertz range. Apart from blanking, it is also used to increase the pulse out-put power of neodym-YAG lasers.

The most frequently used mechanical means of blanking a laser beam is constructed around, and carried out with the aid of, a beam deflector or scan-ner, which will be discussed in detail later on in this book. At the time of writ-ing, it is the most effective way of blanking. Its action causes the laser beam to be deflected from its course. Sometimes, a small pivoted two-pronged fork is used, which is swung into the path of the beam to blank it. Since this can give rise to heating problems, however, the method can be used only with very-low-power lasers. The way this kind of device works is shown in Figure 2-13.

The simplest way of blanking with a mirror, whose longitudinal axis is nor-mally in line with the laser beam, is by turning it around 90° so as to intercept the beam—see Figure 2-14.

21

Figure 2-16
The CATWEAZLE
scanning system

959005-2-10

If the diameter of the laser beam is small, a focusing unit is not needed. When, however, the velocity rises or the diameter is large, the beam is focused on to its its theoretical minimum with two concave lenses. This means that at the focal point fast and reliable blanking becomes possible. Moreover, since the mirror has to blank only a few tenths of a millimeter, the blanking speed is higher. Also, the diverted beam becomes dispersed so that normally no heat sink is needed at the point where it strikes. The mirror used must be of very good quality as otherwise its coating may become damaged by a high-power beam. The construction is shown in Figure 2-15.

The principle of operation just described is still used in some old-fashioned colour mixers to blend a number of single colours into a composite one.

The effort and expense to achieve the required mechanical precision are very high. The lenses must be non-reflective and their surfaces must be smooth and pure to keep any divergence to a minimum and to prevent deterioration of the beam from the focusing unit. After mixing, the three discrete beams must be a coherent entity again so as to give a sharp image at the focal point.

Blanking is also possible by simply turning the beam by means of the beam deflector in the XY scanning unit. This is a fucntional and economic means, and also simple to construct. I has, however, a drawback in that in turning one of the axes is totally included in the output image. Moreover, bouncing or vibra-

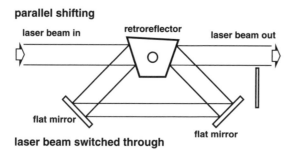

parallel shifting

laser beam in   retroreflector   laser beam out

flat mirror

flat mirror

laser beam switched through

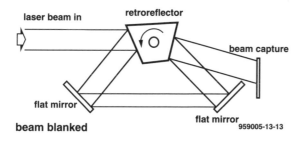

laser beam in   retroreflector

beam capture

flat mirror

flat mirror   959005-13-13

beam blanked

Figure 2-17
Beam blanking by
parallel shifting

tion of the scanner may distort the image. The turning angle is determined by a small analogue circuit which sums the blanking signals of the X-axis and Y-axis.

In spite of a few undoubted flaws, the best mechanical blanking method is parallel shifting. The construction is based on the beam deflector in conjunction with a right-angled prism mirror and two external mirrors. The incident beam is first guided on to the first mirror of the deflector axis, then on to the two deflecting mirrors and the second mirror of the beam deflector, and finally on to the

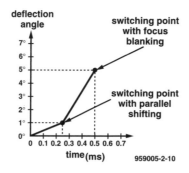

deflection
angle

switching point
with focus
blanking

7°
6°
5°
4°
3°
2°
1°
0°

switching point
with parallel
shifting

0 0.1 0.2 0.3 0.4 0.5 0.6 0.7
time (ms)   959005-2-10

Figure 2-18
Timing diagram of
beam blanking by a
mechanical deflector

23

actual scanning unit. Figure 2-16 illustrates the practical construction of the Catweazle scanning system.

Each mirror functions as a quasi-angle-doubler and path elongator. Even a small rotation of the beam deflector axis produces a large shift of the scanner mirror, resulting in an appreciable gain in velocity. In this method it is possible to achieve a velocity that is almost twice that obtainable with focus blanking. The swivel time when the angle of deflection is 1° is 0.25 ms, but when the angle is 20°, the time is almost doubled. (Test construction: G 120 D with CAT amplifier). Since in parallel shifting an angle of only 1° is needed, the switching time is only 0.25 ms. If the switch-on time is added, the input-to-output transition is only 0.5 ms, corresponding to a frequency of 2 kHz, which is not bad for a mechanical unit. Moreover, the method ensures greater precision of the swivel distance since a smaller angle reduces the bounce

As stated earlier, this method has a few flaws as well. Owing to the number of mirrors used, the losses are greater than in some other systems. For that reason, high-quality, that is, expensive, mirrors with a reflection factor of not less than 95% must be used. Tests with standard mirrors using 1 mm thick coatings have shown that they can be used without difficulties with powers of up to 5 W. Silver-backed or dichroic mirrors must be used with higher powers. Some commercial silver-backed mirrors have a reflection coefficient of 98.5% at wavelengths of 450–700 nm. The reflection coefficient of dichroic mirrors is 99.9%, but such mirrors are very expensive and have flaws themselves, such as incident-angle sensitivity and susceptibility to scratches.

Furthermore, when the beam is directed on to the scanning mirror, the earlier mentioned problem of dispersion occurs. This can be countered to some extent by a non-reflecting edge which the beam hits before the actual scanning mirror at the X-axis or Y-axis. This ensures that the beam cannot be moved across the entire mirror. Because of the virtual absence of vibrations, there is no need for compensating electronic circuits. So, the cost of the mechanical parts is kept within limits, but is nevertheless higher than with focus blanking.

The old-fashioned method of mechanically swivelling the laser beam is slowly but surely superseded by modern means. In this, there are no turning and moving parts: all is done with the aid of modulators. Modulators change the fraction of incident light they transmit in response to external control signals. The modulation may rely on acousto-optic or electro-optic interactions in a suitable crystal.

These crystals enable the laser beam to be blanked, partly by phase shift, partly by rotation of the plane of polarization or by refraction and deflection. The newest generation of crystals can be tuned to a very narrow band in a given range of wavelengths. This enables colour separation to take place, in other words, the crystal acts as a diffraction grating. When various wavelengths are superimposed on to one another, and the different bands are tuned simultaneously, a colour mixing unit is obtained. At the time of writing (late 1996), twelve single lines may be synthesized.

In acousto-optic modulators (AOMs), an acoustic wave sets up a pattern of

959005-13-55

Figure 2-20
PCAOM crystal
for 8 lines

Figure 2-21
Principle of the
PC AOM system

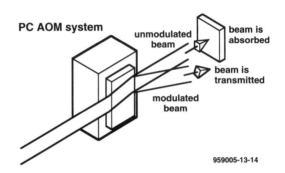

Figure 2-21
Principle of the
PC AOM system

density variations in a crystal with a given refractive index—see Figure 2-19. The laser light is refracted at the glass/air junction at different angles owing to the density variations. The angles are determined by the frequency of the acoustic wave. So as to obtain intensity control, only the refracted beam is used from then on. In most cases, the refracted beam is passed to a laser scanner via an optical-fibre connector. The original beam falls on to the edge of the connector, which serves as collector.

Although there are crystals and drivers that can handle up to 12 separate rays of light, the most frequently used AOMs are 6–8 line versions—see Figure 2-20. The principle of operation is shown in Figure 2-21. The normally used lines are red (676 nm and 647 nm), yellow (568 nm), green (514 nm) and blue (496 nm, 488 nm, 476 nm, and 457 nm). The reason that there are four lines for blue and only one for green and yellow is that the sensitivity of the human eye is not linear: it is greatest at 560 nm. Since green (and yellow) light is strongly present in a mixed-gas laser, whereas blue is not, one line of green suffices, but several lines of blue are needed.

The modulating frequencies for PCAOMs with a power output of about 100 mW are in the range 40–80 MHz. Materials normally used are $PbMoO_4$, TeO_2, Ge, Te, and several types of glass. The efficiency, that is, the usable transmittance, is of the order of 80%, a little lower than obtained with a mechanical RGB unit.

A method just as simple and reliable is illustrated in Figure 2-22. Here, three opto-acoustic modulators mix three filtered lines, red, green and blue obtained from a white-light laser. The intensity of each of the three single colours can be adjusted individually, resulting in typical additive or subtractive colour mixing. This method is more expensive than that using narrow-band modulators since additional, external mechanical parts are required. Also, each modula-

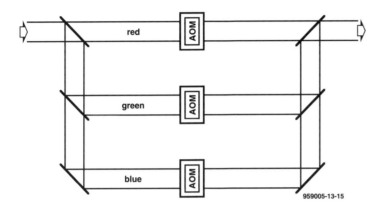

Figure 2-22
Acousto-optic
modulator

tor can modulate only one line, so that in case of a mixed-gas laser large loss-es occur.

Electro-optic modulators rely on the effects of electric fields on the refrac-tive index of certain non-linear materials. Inherent asymmetries within these mate-rials cause them to be birefringent, which means that linearly polarized light with a vertical electric field experiences a different refractive index than linearly polarized light with orthogonal polarization. The application of an electric field (controlled by a capacitor) changes the birefringence, which has the same effect as rotating the polarization of light. When the input light is linearly polarized and a linear polarizing filter is used at the output, such a device can function as a modulator. The extent to which the polarization is rotated determines how much light will be transmitted by the output polarizer.

Electro-optic modulators are available in several sizes, power outputs and frequency ranges. For instance, a Conoptics Model 8890-370 has an optical bandwidth of 400–800 nm with an aperture of 2.5 mm. Attenuation is 300 at 488 nm and 500 at 633 nm. Transmittance is specified as 85%. The earlier mentioned capacitor has a value of 90 pF. The permissible optical output is 3.5 W mm^{-2}, which, with the aperture specified (4.9 mm^2) gives a total of 17 W.

Typical bandwidths are of the order of 100 MHz, but peak modulating fre-quencies may exceed 1 GHz. Such figures cannot be obtained with mechan-ical modulation, although this normally has a much better efficiency. For instance, a first-class mirror may have an efficiency of 99%, so that losses are negligible, whereas in case of a crystal 15% is considered good.

Modulators are used for the rapid moving of a laser beam, stabilizing the intensity of a laser beam, superimposing high-frequency side bands on to a carrier beam, or the transmission of optical data.

Figure 2-23
Mirror holder
with fine
adjustment

959005-13-57

An advantage of semiconductor lasers is that their output beam can be moved directly. Good diode models have a modulation input via which the laser beam can be blanked completely without loss. Such lasers are used in small projector systems where they do not need additional hardware. Modulation frequencies may extend into the GHz region where, however, large modulation factors cannot be achieved. On the other hand, a modulation depth of 100% is readily obtained in the MHz bands.

The control of the modulators and deflectors described so far is achieved invariably by a computer or pulse system. This is not always necessary, however. A laser beam may be blanked simply by interrupting it with a rotating wheel. High interrupting rates cannot be achieved with a shutter, but rather better results are possible with the wheel. The rotating wheel is a glass disk on which a large segments or several segments, depending on the required blanking rate, are painted black. The black areas interrupt the beam when the disk is being rotated. The speed of rotation and the amount of blacking determine the modulating frequency, that is, the pulse-pause ratio of the beam. If the disk is controlled by a servo motor, the pulse-pause ratio can be held very stable.

2.6 Scanners (beam deflectors)

Beam deflectors currently provide the only practical method of deflecting a multicoloured laser beam rapidly and accurately. There are other methods, but these have generally not been nearly as successful as the beam deflector. There are two types of scanner: open-loop and closed-loop also called feedback.

Open-loop scanners, that is, deflecting units without a closed positioning circuit, are not very accurate and not really intended for precise positioning. Owing to the absence of a position detector on the spindle, it is impossible for the actual position of the spindle to be determined. True, the spindle moves to the approximate position contained in the control signal, but various factors cause the position to shift about. One of these factors is the magnetic hysteresis of the inductor and the soft iron core; others are the varying operating temperature and the unequal load distribution of the moving mass. Today, this type of beam deflector is therefore used only in simple scanning applications, such as those for radiation or for obtaining Lissajous effects, and in certain simple graphics applications. This situation may change, however.

Recently, so-called accelerator drivers have become available. These provide very large current feedback factors coupled with modern, accurate scanner mechanics, and very high speeds. The nominal and operating currents through the coil of the deflector are likened continuously by an accurate current comparator. The slightest difference is amplified by a measurement amplifier and fed back to the scanner mechanics. In this way, accuracies of up to 70% of those obtainable with closed-loop deflectors can be achieved. Nevertheless, these circuits are very sensitive to temperature changes and must not be used for positioning a laser beam without due consideration. On the other hand, the much lower price of this kind of system, compared with the closed-loop type, must also be borne in mind. All in all, by virtue of the high scanning rates and large angles of deflection obtainable, fairly complex graphics applications can use this arrangement, as long as there is no stringent requirement for linearity and accuracy of position.

Closed-loop scanners may be divided into several sub-divisions. One of these comprises general-purpose scanners, which were the first functional deflectors and are still among the better ones. Their construction is relatively simple. Fitted to one end of a spindle on double bearings is a small torsion bar, the other end of which is fixed permanently to the housing. This bar arranges the spindle in a predetermined null position. Also linked to the spindle is a star-shaped fixed magnet, which is surrounded by an electromagnet whose hysteresis must be as small as possible. When a current flows through the coil of the electromagnet, a magnetic field is set up that moves the spindle in one of two directions, depending on the sense of the current. Also linked to the spindle is a position detector which tells the electronic control circuit the exact actual position of the spindle. The electronic circuit continually compares the nominal input signal with the actual one from the sensor, and alters the current through the electromagnet until the desired position has been reached. There is a drawback to this arrangement in that the reluctance of the torsion bar must be compensated by an electric force which causes losses and heat dissipation. When the deflector warms up, the characteristic operating curve changes. This in turn causes a change in the exact position of the laser beam so that further compensation is required.

There are, of course, methods to avoid these difficulties, and new ones are constantly being developed. Unfortunately, most solutions to the problems bring new difficulties of their own. To start with, the new generation of beam deflectors no longer uses torsion bars and reset springs, but the remainder of the design has remained the same. A permanent or electro-magnet is fitted on the spindle, which is linked to a position sensor. The journals of the spindle are contained in resonance-free bearings. The exact positioning of the spindle is effected entirely by electronic circuits. Once the desired position has been reached, the operating current may be all but switched off since there is no restoring force. This means that little power is required to drive the deflector. The spindle has little mass and little inertia, which is beneficial to the speed of operation. Low heat dissipation ensures that there is little non-linearity and this enables exact positioning. But even here there may be a problem. If, for instance, the driver is wrongly adjusted and it applies strong control pulses to the mechanical drive, the entire system may begin to vibrate. The stronger these vibrations are, the larger the current drain and heat dissipation. Moreover, in the long term, the life of the scanner will be adversely affected.

The latest development, which promises to become a leader in the field of rotating-mirror scanners is the scanner developed by Cambridge Technology (see Figure 2-24). In this, the spindle is accurately positioned on the basis of optical feedback. Mass has been kept to a minimum by omitting a mirror holder. Instead, the mirror is glued in a small slit in the upper side of the spindle. This kind of fast deflector has a specified response time of 250 μs for a 5° shift, which agrees fairly well with what we measured in practice. Since it can provide an optical deflection of 80° (response time 1 ms!), it is ideal for use in beam positioning systems. Even at that deflection, a response time of 1 ms is possible with, of course, the aid of the appropriate drivers.

Compared with the G120 from General Scanning there are some disadvantages associated with this construction: the increased sensitivity to temperature makes a good heat sink imperative, and the poor connections (a simple 10-way header) increases the risk of vibration. Also, a replaceable fuse to protect the deflectors is fitted on a small board at the rear of the enclosure, but since this

Figure 2-24
Beam deflector from
Cambridge
Technology

is mounted so close to the casing, replacing it is a very tedious job. Furthermore, the amplifier circuits have a current limiting network that is actuated when the scanners are overdriven; in some cases, this is definitely detrimental. Nevertheless, extensive tests have shown that the gain in speed is about 20 per cent but in spite of that many users prefer the more robust G120.

A different version of torsion-less beam deflector was introduced not so long ago. This consists of a sort of stepper motor with a fairly large step (angle) of 25°. Within this step, the spindle of the motor can rotate freely. Powerful magnets in the motor ensure good efficiency. A small mirror is mounted at an angle of 45° on the part of the spindle that protrudes from the rear of the motor. A small LED with a focusing lens is fitted at right angles to the same part of the spindle. The light emitted by the LED falls on to the mirror and, after reflection at an angle of 90°, on a linear optical sensor. Because of the rotation of the spindle, the focus of the LED moves to and fro over the sensor and so produces a fairly accurate feedback signal for the control electronics.

Each scanner must be adjusted separately so as to compensate for tolerances in the control electronics and the sensor. According to the manufacturers' specification, very high speeds of the order of 24 000 dots per second can be attained; this corresponds to a response time of 180 μs. However, measurements in the laboratory gave a maximum speed of 9 000 dots per second, which is much lower than that of the well-known G120D from General Scanning. When we reported this to the manufacturer, we were told that new amplifiers and deflectors giving speeds of up to 30 000 dots per second were being tested.

A further qualification test concerns the accuracy, but a discussion of the results would not mean much, because the accuracy depends on a number of factors. One of these is the air, or rather, the dust in the air. In spite of the internal electronics and angle sensor being encased, there is a risk that dust and grime may be deposited on to the sensor and so influence the measurement results, and this would, of course, prevent the control electronics from functioning properly. Even the slightest non-linearity of the sensor results in less than accurate beam control.

In spite of all kinds of set-back, researchers continue to experiment with new systems with variable success and always with three aims in mind : to make it faster, more accurate and less expensive. Just recently, ITT introduced a chip on to the market that contains hundreds of tiny mirrors which can all be pointed very rapidly in the same direction. However, when used with a powerful laser, there is a risk that the chip gets damaged or destroyed. Also, the optical accuracy at long distances needs to be improved. Another development concerns a deflection unit based on crystals that offers some advantages, but also has a number of disadvantages. Some parameters: deflection angle 2°; deflection frequency about 250 kHz; only one wavelength can be deflected; it is expensive (about $US4000). No doubt, there will be further interesting developments in the next few years.

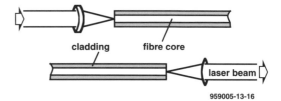

Figure 2-25 Coupling of a laser beam to an optical fibre

2.7 Power transmission via optical fibre

The most serious difficulty for a laser user who needs lots of power concerns the physical dimensions of the laser. An argon laser with a power of 6–8 W is three feet (1 metre) long and weighs 55 pounds (25 kg), while one with a power of 15–20 W is six feet six inches (2 metres) long and weighs about 130 pounds (60 kg). Clearly, such a unit cannot easily be carried around, but fortunately, the laser light may be transported over distances of up to three hundred feet (100 metres) via optical-fibre cable. However, this also has its drawbacks. But, let us consider its very real advantages first.

To hold a laser beam, to light a cigarette with it, to cut paper or what have you with it is a delightful experience. All these are possible with the use of optical fibre. A cable made of such fibres can transfer the laser light over distances of up to three hundred feet to positions where the laser itself could not be located. Powerful laser light transported via a 50 μm (0.05 mm) thick optical fibre, at the end of which it is reconverted by a small lens to its original beam width offers a great many interesting applications. If a fibre of 50 μm is too thick, one of 30 μm or even 25 μm can be used. The thinner the fibre, the smaller the divergence at the output, but the lower the efficiency.

Figure 2-25 shows a b asic optical-fibre system, including the input and output coupling optics. The laser beam is coupled into the system with the aid of an achromatic lens, consisting of at least two component lenses. An achromatic lens is needed because the laser light consists of a number of colours, each of which has a different frequency. If a single lens were used, the focus of each of the colours would be in a different position, and this means that colour correction is required, which is provided by an achromatic lens (see Figure 2-26).

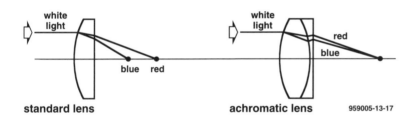

standard lens   achromatic lens   959005-13-17

Figure 2-26
How an
achromatic lens works

Wideband dereflection prevents random reflections and increases the efficiency of the system. The focus of the lens coincides with the point where the laser beam enters the optical fibre. The beam must fall head on and exactly in the middle of the fibre to prevent the fibre being damaged and to ensure optimum transfer of light. The laser light is then transported through the fibre and output at the other end. Since it is then strongly divergent, a second lens is needed to reconvert it to a coherent beam. Colour correction at the output is not very important: even a simple convex lens gives good results.

It is, of course, imperative that the ends of the fibre are as smooth as possible to prevent dispersion and reflections. A rough end is a certain way of ensuring a short life and poor efficiency. Also, the optical quality of the transmitted light is poor. This means that the output beam no longer resembles the input beam, but rather that of a multimode laser. This can be seen clearly when the output beam is directed on to a white surface without the use of a focusing lens. This shows another interesting effect as well. When the end of the fibre is held steady and the fibre is moved about at some distance from the end, the structure within the focus changes: it is as if a number of fireflies are moving about in it. These dots of light and dark areas are the result of interference within the fibre. The innumerable photons that are reflected within the fibre follow paths of different lengths. Wave peaks and troughs may be superimposed on to the light, which may lead to extinction or amplification if two peaks coincide. If we would have a very sensitive measuring instrument that could be held steady within the light cone, we would continuously measure tiny power variations. When these are distributed over the entire surface, they are no longer discernible. Later on, a useful application of the interference phenomenon will be discussed.

The typical efficiency of energy transfer via optical fibre is 60–90 per cent, depending on the construction and quality of the optical components, and the surface accuracy within the fibre and at its ends. Coupling a high-power laser beam into an optical fibre requires extreme care and precision.

In practice, a laser beam is coupled into an optical fibre with the aid of fixed optics. First, the laser is ignited and adjusted for minimum power output. The coupling is put into position in front of the laser. The beam is coarsely centred with the aid of a small, thick piece of perspex in which a hole has been drilled in the centre. The optical fibre is inserted into the hole and fastened with the coupling nut. A faint light should then be evident at the other end of the fibre. If this is not so, the foregoing procedure has to be repeated. A first operating point is found by moving the coupling mechanism in a vertical and/or horizontal direction. The coupling is turned over in two directions that are at right angles to one another and moved about in a horizontal and / or vertical direction again until an optimum operating point is found. An experienced operator may accomplish this in a few minutes, but a beginner may well take half a day. Practice makes perfect!

In the transmission of data via optical fibre, power is of secondary importance. In this application, use is made of semiconductor lasers where the priorities are different. Nevertheless, a good efficiency remains of great importance since often fairly large distances have to be spanned. Since the transmission is digital, it does not matter how many booster amplifiers there are between input and output. Bits and bytes do not easily get lost!

In essence, the principle of optical data transmission is fairly simple, but the details are complex. One single fibre may simultaneously carry some hundreds of telephone conversations, several television or radio channels and a number of data communication channels. The laser light is modulated into large packets that are analysed at the receiving end by a computer and then switched through to the correct addressee. A simpler solution makes use of modulated carrier waves. Just as in broadband cable communication, several frequencies are sent through the fibre, each of which may be modulated. Because of narrow-band receivers a large number of such carrier waves can be sent simultaneously through a single fibre. The whole system is appreciably simpler than a multi-core telephone cable. Long-distance systems use small amplifiers at regular intervals, so that losses remain small. The optical-fibre cable contains a multi-core copper conductor that carries the supply for these amplifiers. Since the design of digital amplifiers is simpler and more reliable than analogue ones, digital amplifiers dominate in modern systems. Such systems are, of course, eminently suitable for use in an Integrated Services Digital Network (ISDN), but they are also of great importance for telephone and fax communications, videophones, on-line data transmissions, and many others.

2.8 Laser weapons

In the inexorable march of technology into the defence industries of the big powers, the laser was not overlooked. When the first laser was announced in the early 1960s, military scientists immediately saw in it a weapon of immense power to combat their imagined enemies. Within a very short time, laser technology became involved in all sorts of research project. Ideas came hard and fast and were acted upon rapidly; money became freely available and was spent at a tremendous rate. It was only slowly that the boffins came to the conclusion that destruction of enemy weapons with lasers was not as simple as originally thought. The spaceship *Enterprise* regularly makes use of laser weapons, but that is pure science fiction. It was found at an early stage that there was still a long way to go before the laser was suitable for military purposes. For a long time, the American Strategic Defense Initiative (SDI – also known as Star Wars) was considered by western governments to be quintessential for the survival of the United States and the rest of the western world.

The powers required from the lasers used in that project were gigantic and had to be provided by chemical lasers. These one-off lasers could fire only once but that was thought to be sufficient to intercept an intercontinental ballistic missile (IBM). The intention was to have large numbers of such lasers on board satellites in geostationary orbit over the United States form a watertight defence network.

The realization of the system was started and created thousands of jobs. Scientific minds created utopian ideas of defences against defences against defences. The western world would again have a clear superiority over the Soviet Union in the armaments race. These ideas were soon scuppered, however, when it was discovered that a high-gloss coating on a racket would be sufficient to reflect a laser beam and render it impotent. Fortunately, the end of the Cold War put a stop to all these ideas. As a matter of interest, there are still many people today who believe that the SDI was a scheme between the United States and the Soviet Union.

However, this was not the end of laser technology as far as the military were concerned. The early rough and unmanageable power lasers could not be used effectively against an enemy. The energy sources required for the generation of the laser beams were also much too bulky. It was only at a later stage, with the advent of semiconductor lasers that small yet powerful highly directional weapons became possible. The most serious problems in these are the relatively large losses and the consequent low efficiency. For instance, to obtain a useful output power from an argon laser, a continuous input power of several kilowatts is required. Where would that come from? A much better unit is a CO_2 laser, which is wellnigh ideal with an efficiency of almost 10 per cent. However, its practical use is handicapped by its vulnerability and the large dimensions of the laser tube.

It is not surprising that serious developments had to wait for the semiconductor laser. These also have a maximum efficiency of about 10 per cent, but the laser diodes are much smalle.. This has the problem that a large dissipation must be radiated by a small area. Powerful laser diodes are therefore normally provided with their own cooling system. This, however, requires energy and increases the weight of the laser. All these are reasons why the first laser applications were not suitable for military purposes.

The guns or rocket launchers in most modern tanks are equipped with laser guidance systems. These are also used with hand guns, grenade throwers and mortars. The latest development is a system that 'only' blinds enemy soldiers for a period, but does not kill them. Who said that war was becoming more humane? Indeed, has the word humane any significance in military parlance?

Laser weapons have recently also become available to the electronics amateur. Anyone interested in the United States can buy a book dealing with DIY electronic weapons, including a high-power laser weapon! The book is of interest even to pacifists. Also in the United States, electronic guidance systems for 'normal' weapons such as hand guns, rifles, hand bows and cross bows are freely available. In its simplest form, such a system projects a small dot of light on to the target indicating the spot where the bullet or arrow will hit. Members of archery and rifle clubs use such equipment in practice to improve their accuracy and concentration.

Some years ago a development intended for the civil market was announced in Austria. An inventor there, in conjunction with a professional hunter, had developed a telesopic sight with integral rangefinder. This enables the marksman to adapt his rifle's firepower or sight adjustment to the distance. The inevitable result is a much greater number of hits. This development can be taken a step further by combining it with an automatic homing device. The velocity and weight of the bullet are input into an integral computer via a small keyboard, and the computer sets the sight, depending on the distance of the target. All the marksman then has to do is hold the gun steady and pull the trigger.

Considering the weight and dimensions of current power lasers, we need not be concerned about the introduction of portable laser weapons in the near future. Nevertheless, some relatively small pulsed lasers already produce powers that make one suspect that a truly portable laser will become available early in the next century. It will certainly change the face of warfare.

The energy source for such a laser would be a battery carried in a kitbag (rucksack). As the size of batteries gets smaller and smaller, the capacity and power of the laser increases. A solid-state laser produces pulses of some kilowatts and these would temporarily blind, but not kill, enemy soldiers. The laser beam would be effective even at relatively long distances.

It is not the intention of this book to dwell too long on the application of lasers as weapons. Most well-thinking people are no doubt against this, but even they must accept that laser technology would not be at the stage it is now without the large rersearch budgets allocated to the defence industry. Virtually all breakthroughs in the areas of miniaturization, larger arithmetic powers of processors, and the development of all kinds of laser have been the result of well-directed research in government R&D (research and development) establishments. It would be wrong, however, to remain jubilant about this and to that end I want to show the reader what is already available for sale in this area. I will show how a laser weapon is constructed and taken into use. The reader should, of course, not consider this as a construction project and for that reason the component values in Figure 2-27 have been deliberately omitted. The reader is advised not to try to find them out by trial and error. The description and illustration have been included for completeness' sake only. As an aside: secrete services such as MI5 and the CIA recognized the immense capabilities of the laser at an early stage. In *Goldfinger*, Ian Fleming's famous book published in the late 1950s (and later made into an even more famous film), Goldfinger keeps agent James Bond 007 at bay with an enormous laser. (Did you know, by the way, that 007 is the international country code for Russia?)

Pulsed-laser gun
As mentioned earlier, this laser originated in the United States. The underlying technology shows how relatively easy it is to build a powerful weapon from simple and easily available parts. The laser consists of a current source, a pulsed diode laser and the requisite control electronics. Depending on the power of the laser, the current source is built into the stock or contained in a small bag carried on the back or on a belt. Various diode lasers produce powers of a few watts to 50 W and more. Many modern versions can deliver even larger powers, depending on the duration of the shot. The system described here uses a diode with a pulse power of 35 W which can be set to a firing rate of 50–2000 pulses per second. The electronic circuits are contained in a tubular enclosure, which also houses the laser diode and a collimator lens to obtain a parallel beam. The tube is mounted on a round enclosure that houses the battery and control electronics. This enclosure is provided with a handle that contains the trigger. The assembly can easily be fitted with a telescopic sight or homing laser. The result is a hand gun or rifle with a range of a couple of hundred meters (300 ft or so).

Warning!
The equipment produces low to medium power infra-red pulses with a repetition rate of up to 2000 pulses per second. Its use is illegal. You must never point the weapon at other persons or on to reflecting surfaces. During testing of the equipment always use suitable safety goggles and

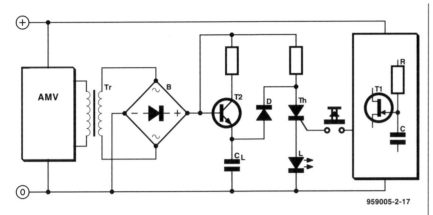

959005-2-17

Figure 2-27
Basic circuit of a
pulsed-laser hand
weapon

make absolutely sure that there are no unprotected people nearby. Never look into the equipment when the electronic circuits are powered, not even in the standby mode.

Operation

A laser diode is nothing but a three-layer semiconductor: the p-n junction (potential barrier) between an n-layer of silicon, a p-layer of gallium arsenide, and a layer of doped gallium arsenide. The n-material contains electrons that pass through the p-n junction and recombine with the holes in the p-material. In this way, holes in the p-material are transferred to the n-material. Without an external current source, the diode is in equilibrium. When a voltage is applied across the diode, the potential barrier is lowered and a large stream of electrons flows itowards the p-material. If the voltage is applied with reverse polarity, more holes are created in the p-material, the potential barrier is increased an no current can flow. If, therefore, a voltage of correct polarity is applied, electrons begin to move instantly from the n-material to the p-material. When an electron and a hole recombine, a photon is emitted. These photons are, however, not yet coherent. To make them coherent, a closed resonator is required from which the photons can escape in only one direction. So, to produce a laser beam, the following are required:

1. enough electrons that reach the requisite energy level, and
2. an optical resonator that encloses the generated photons and so causes even more photons to be emitted.

The number of energy-rich photons is determined by the supply current. The generated beam is reflected at the ends of the silicon crystal, where, owing to the refractive index between silicon and air, a reflective layer is situated. Starting energy is imparted to the electrons in the p-n junction. When these electrons pass into the p-region, they collide with photons that are already moving to and fro in the resonator, whereby new photons are emitted. This is how the laser action is established.

Control electronics
The diagram of the basic electronic control circuit is shown in Figure 2-27. A simple free-running multivibrator and a transformer generate a trapezoidal control pulse of 200–225 V, which is passed to a thyristor via a unijunction transistor. The thyristor delivers a high-tension pulse to the laser diode. The resistor and reservoir capacitor at the gate of the transistor determine the pulse rate. The maximum pulse rate depends on the capacity of the battery providing the power supply. The energy stored in the capacitor is discharged in one burst across the laser diode to produce a powerful laser pulse. The rise time of this pulse is determined by the thyristor and the decay time by the reservoir capacitor.

When the thyristor is connected in the traditional manner, the anode current of the laser diode, which is switched on by the pulse at the gate, reaches its maximum value within a microsecond. In this time, the anode-to-cathode resistance drops from infinite to a fraction of an ohm. Normally, a pulse is shorter than the switch-on time of the thyristor, which results in a diode impedance of about 1–10 Ω. Considering that the reservoir capacitor is charged to a potential of about 400 V and is discharged via a resistance of not more than 10 Ω, the resulting current is not less than 40 A. This means that the connecting leads between diode, capacitor and thyristor must have a diameter that can handle this level of current without problems.

It is worth while to experiment with various types of thyristor, since each type has a specific rise time. The reservoir capacitor should be a paper, or metal film polyester type. Ceramic capacitors are not recommended since these can be discharged only (relatively) slowly owing to their large internal resistance. Best results are obtained with a polyester film capacitor. Its breakdown voltage must be equal to at least the fully-charged potential, but preferably 20 per cent or more higher.

To make sure that the pulse current does not exceed the short-circuit current, a low-value resistor has been included in the discharge circuit. A value of 1–2 Ω should be adequate. Great care must be taken in the wiring of the high-tension discharge circuit. Long leads have a self-inductance that may affect the pulse rate adversely, so that the diode and discharge circuit must be as close together as feasible. The length of the leads connecting the high-tension cascade and the discharge circuit is not important. Since only small currents flow in the power supply, and there are also no steep pulse edges, the supply may be external or in a separate section of the overall enclosure.

This concludes the basic description of the pulsed-laser gun. Again, it is not a construction project!

Real laser weapons
There are no construction details or descriptions available for real laser weapons; in any case, building one is strongly discouraged. Nevertheless, they form an interesting part of the history of the laser.

In 1983, Ronald Reagan, then president of the United States, broadcast his now famous Star Wars speech. Encouraged by the scientific successes in laser research in the United States, the president promised that a powerful defence shield against nuclear attacks would be put in place in the space above the United States. The project would create tens of thousands of new jobs – a promise that always augurs well with a population.

It seemed then to many that the dreams of science-fiction books and films were about to become reality. However, right from the onset the spiritual fathers and managers of the SDI project doubted whether the envisaged systems and mega-power lasers could be realized in the near future. Many parts of the project were delayed or even (temporarily) stopped not only by technical problems but also by financial dificulties. Even today, although vast sums are still being pumped into laser research, the original aim of the project, that is, to launch laser satellites in orbit around the earth, is still far in the future.

As temporary measures, schemes were devised to shoot down enemy satellites with terrestrial lasers. Systems were developed to distinguish real nuclear heads from dummy ones. Only much later would high-power lasers be used directly against enemy rockets. The end of the Cold War put a stop to most parts of the project.

Reverting to the original plans of the Pentagon, however, the heart of the laser weapon system was to be formed by an X-ray laser. In such a laser, a nuclear explosion produces extremely powerful X-rays with which a laser action is effected in a solid-state medium. Because of the coherence of the generated radiation, a very strong beam of X-rays is generated that can penetrate almost anything. The energy-rich beams would be directed on to targets by a large number of laser tubes fitted around the nuclear war head. Since nuclear weapons are used in the project, all details are top secret. Nevertheless, it is at odds with Reagan's promise that the SDI project would be 'non-nuclear'. Even more frightening is the fact that, if the system is ever actually developed, it will have to be tested in space and this means that nuclear explosions would take place in space. This would be a flagrant violation of the 1963 Treaty not to conduct above-ground nuclear tests.

Nuclear-explosion-fed lasers are no whim of the imagination, however. As early as 1981, successful underground tests have been carried out with lasers that were pumped by powerful explosions. Some of these tests were conducted in California. It is assumed that these top secret tests were made public by the creators themselves. Lowell Wood, a disciple of the father of the hydrogen bomb, Edward Teller, appears to have used them for his own purposes. Shortly afterwards, both scientists alleged that dramtic progress had been made in the research into X-ray lasers. Many other researchers thought these allegations premature. The idea was to have available in the so-called Phase 1 an energy and defence potential with which at least some of the attacking nuclear heads could be neutralized. But the budget for even this modest system had to be pruned in 1988 to about $70bn.

In spite of earlier prognoses, there is no mention of lasers in Phase 1, indicating that this phase would have to be operational without the heart of the system. In place of a beam of energy, conventional kinetic weapons were to be used. One group of such weapons, located on board satellites, were to throw attacking rockets off course by means of collision or explosion. A second group would be stationed on earth but controlled by satellite.

Phase 2 is not yet fully determined. It is possible that some laser satellites will support the kinetic weapons. To do so would, however, require a suitable carrier rocket and this has not yet been developed. But, assuming that this would be ready, which type of laser would be the prime candidate?

Since enormous amounts of energy are needed, and the space on board satellites is limited, researchers, as already mentioned, are in favour of X-ray lasers actuated by nuclear explosions. In spite of their tiny dimensions, these lasers produce an unimaginable amount of energy.

Another candidate is the chemical laser which derives its energy from the reaction of certain elements such as hydrogen and fluorine. The generated radiation lies in the infra-red region with a wavelength of about 2600 nm. One of the first usable of these lasers, the 'alpha' model, is reputed to have an output power of more than 5 megawatts.

The solid-state pulsed laser

Readers who cannot get excited about the earlier described hand gun with laser diode may like the following description of a solid-state pulsed laser. However, owing to the danger in building and using this laser, readers are strongly advised not to to attempt to build it.

Warning

A solid-state laser of the type described in this section combines a dangerously high operating voltage with an equally dangerous amount of pulsed light energy. Readers without the necessary specialist knowledge are strongly advised against experimenting with these systems.

Fundamentally, a solid-state laser is fairly simple. It is based on a crystal, in this description a rod of ruby. As we have seen at the beginning of this chapter, the first laser was a ruby laser. Building such a laser therefore has a certain amount of nostalgia.

A flashlamp is fitted around the rod of synthetic ruby. This can be done in several ways, but the efficiency will depend to a large extent on the correct geometry. Both ends of the rod are silver-coated to make them reflective (although modern ruby lasers use separate mirrors, one totally reflecting and one partly transparent). For our purpose, the rod with coated ends will be described: this prevents any problems with maladjusted resonators. These resonator mirrors form a very important part of the system. Apart from them, all that is needed (but essentially so) are the control electronics for the flashlamp and a cooling system for the ruby rod.

A laser so constructed can generate short pulses with enormous power density: values of a few megawatts are not exceptional. Let us assume that we have a flashlamp producing an energy of 1000 joules that is optimally matched to the ruby rod. Assuming a pulse of 1 ms length and a pump energy of 1000 joules, the relationship watt = joule / second gives us a power of

1000/0.001 = 1 000 000 W.

Even if the efficiency is only 0.1%, the optical power of the emerging laser beam is still 1000 W. When the pulse duration is controlled with the aid of a Q-switch between the resonators and set to, say, 10 μs, the resulting pulsed optical power is

(1000/0.00001) × 0.1 = 100 000 W.

This is a seemingly impossible but very impressive figure. If one could construct such a monstrous machine it would be necessary to build a solid brick wall to serve as 'bullet stopper'. And, what is even more important: do wear suitable safety goggles at all times!

The basic construction was already shown in Figure 2-1. Good optical coupling between flashlamp and ruby rod is of paramount importance. A spiral-shaped flashlamp is excellent. The flashlamp is surrounded by a polished coated reflector whose sides are made as light-proof as possible. This construction gives a good efficiency, but also suffers from much heat loss. This means that only few short-duration pulses can be generated. With the power levels shown in the foregoing paragraph and without forced cooling, only one pulse per minute would be possible. A higher rate would lead to a dangerous increase in heat loss in the flashlamp and ruby rod. A higher pump rate is possible only if forced cooling, air or water, or cooling with a heat exchanger and compressor system is used.

The flashlamp is driven by a conventional discharge circuit such as that of an electronic flash. Complete construction kits for this are available from mail-order firms or specialist electronics retailers. Initially, a standard flashlamp is perfectly suitable. For a professional construction, the ruby rod and flashlamp must be tuned to one another. Used ruby rods are sometimes available at very reasonable prices.

If you do not want to use Q-switching, you have to take a ruby rod with silver-coated reflecting ends to construct a small, user-friendly laser system for domestic applications. The rod and the flashlamp may be housed in a cylindrical enclosure. Because of the heat dissipation and the high supply voltages, it is advisable to fit the control electronics in a separate tube mounted at the underside of the main enclosure. The battery must be a large-capacity type and is therefore fairly large – it is best to carry this with a belt around your waist.

A small diode laser, parallel to the laser tube proper, makes hitting the target easier – but never aim it at a living being! The supply for a diode laser may be a much smaller battery than needed with a ruby laser, while it can be operated by a simple microswitch.

What does the future hold?

Research into smaller, more efficient, and more powerful lasers continues unabated. The end of the Cold War has put a stop to the SDI project. Today, more 'humane' ways of warfare have the highest priority, and the laser seems to fit that bill well. The solid-state weapons described earlier may become available in rifle-form within a few years. The soldier of the future already exists and is being trained in modern warfare. In this, the laser is not intended as a lethal weapon, but as a means of temporarily taking enemy soldiers out of action by blinding or wounding slightly.

Soldiers so equipped carry the control electronics and battery in a kit-bag on the back and have the rifle-like laser weapon in their hands. It appears to be the intention to blind the opponent, because there is no way that the human eye can be protected effectively against the laser beam. Of course, the opponent will wear safety goggles, but how does he know what wavelength the other party is using. Safety goggles suitable as protection against all wavelengths would blind him as effectively as a direct hit from a laser rifle.

Laser homing equipment has also come into operation; currently it is already in use with mortars and howitzers. The sight is loosely aimed at the intended target after which the electronics does the rest. Distance setting, computing the ballistic trajectory of the projectile, and servo tracking of the target – all these are no longer a problem.

However regrettable the development and use of weapons may be, it is a fact that even convinced pacifists cannot deny the importance of military research. Without that research, lasers used in hospitals would not be of the high level they are today.

2.9 Lasers in medicine

One of the dreams of mankind, the painless operation, is slowly becoming reality. Where not so long ago crude (relatively speaking) scalpels did the work in the operating theatre, lasers are now used for more and more operations that used to mean bloody and painful affairs. The laser scalpel has been a commonplace in ophthalmology for years; lasers are being used to pulverize gall stones; and lasers help dentists to treat their patients in a painless manner. All this has become possible thanks to modern laser technology and developments in the field of power transmission via optical fibre. Where conventional scalpels used to make bleeding wounds that had to be clamped and then sutured, today lasers seal the edges of the incision at the same time as making it. Where not so long ago a dentist had to use a drill, he/she can now vaporize the affected parts of a tooth. All the patient notices is a slight smell of singeing and even this is easily removed by a small extractor fan. Operations for the removal of tumours, removal of undesired tattoo marks, reattaching a displaced retina, all these have become routine operations that are carried out thousands of times a year. Even in acupuncture, a tiny He-Ne laser is often used today instead of needles. Half a milliwatt is more than enough to stimulate nerve ends at the correct place. Large, open wounds have proved to heal more rapidly when irradiated with laser light. One day we all might treat ourselves at home armed with a laser pen and an instruction booklet!

The first successful operation by laser was carried out in 1972 in Tel Aviv, when a patient had a malignant tumour removed from her right breast. This operation proved so simple and was so successful that the entire medical world became interested. The laser was a CO_2 type whose light was directed on to the laser scalpel via a swivelling arm. The operation was an experiment or, rather, served as a comparison between the conventional and the new method. It proved to be no contest: the laser method won handsomely: not only did the operating wound heal much more quickly, but there was also a substantial reduction in loss of blood and, last but not least, since the laser light is totally sterile, there was hardly any risk of infection.

Another highlight of this method of operating was the removal of a brain tumour with the aid of a CO_2 laser at the University Clinic for Neurosurgery in Graz, Austria. This operation was not followed by the in other methods inevitable and dangerous bleeding in the brain cavity, so that it was a complete success. In fact, the patient was back on his feet within a week. Further comparable successes quickly confirmed the value of this method of operating.

Even before the invention of the laser, ophthalmologists used beams of intense light to reattach a displaced retina to the eye ball. When the first laser was announced, the interest of ophthalmic surgeons the world over was aroused. Unfortunately, the ruby laser, which generates only short pulses, could not be used for such eye operations. These had to wait for the argon-ion gas laser, whose wavelength is ideal for this kind of operation. Today, there are many thousands of lasers used in ophthalmic clinics and practices. In these, the light of an argon laser with a power of a few hundred milliwatts is directed to a light pen via an optical fibre system. With the resulting coherent and very thin beam of light, the retina is reattached accurately and without any risk.

When in the past kidney stones, which make urinating torture, had to be removed, there was no option but to cut open the patient. This was a serious operation followed by a lengthy period of recuperation. Thanks to the laser, this has become a much simpler operation virtually without risk to the patient. Laser beams of a certain wavelength do not cut through the stone, but pulverize it. When the pulses of an neodymium laser are directed on to a kidney stone, this disintegrates totally and the tiny fragments leave the body of the patient naturally. The entire operation is over within a few seconds and is virtually painless.

Spectacular operations with a laser are now a commonplace. Only the imagination of the user limits the possibilities of the laser. Even a life-threatening ailment like arteriosclerosis (calcification of arteries) can be treated. This is done 'simply' by cutting a lengthways opening in the affected blood vessel, whereupon the blood can flow freely again, which (for instance) may prevent the risk of a heart attack.

Medical researchers are attempting to selectively destroy cancer cells with the aid of dye lasers. Use is made in this of the altered characteristics of cancerous cells. Because of mutatition, such cells absorb a different wavelength than healthy cells. This knowledge enables cancerous cells to be destroyed while healthy tissues are not affected.

Many more developments in the application of lasers in the field of medicine may be expected in the future. It is already certain that the laser has earned a permanent place in the medical world.

2.10 Lasers in materials processing

The application of lasers in materials processing has become such an all-encompassing subject that its description would take a whole book by itself. In this section, only some of the most important and interesting ones will therefore be described.

Many tools and equipment available in any reasonable hardware store are marked and inscribed with instructions and measurements with the aid of lasers. Micrometers, vernier callipers, rulers, even ballpens and car headlights are marked faster and more simply than with the etching techniques of yesteryear. Owing to the compact construction and the required large powers, Nd:YAG lasers are used almost exclusively for these processes. Moreover, the short wavelength of these lasers is beneficial for the absorption of the light beam by the material being processed. If a wavelength of 1064 nm is too long for the pure processing of a certain material, a frequency doubler may be used to reduce the wavelength to 532 nm (green light) so that even 'difficult' materials can be worked on. Paper, plastics, perspec, wood, aluminium, steel, titanium, ceramics – they can all be inscribed indelibly and scratch-resistant.

Many metal processing firms have concluded some time ago that welding by laser is appreciably more efficient and longer-lasting than conventional arc or gas welding. The weld is neater and tighter so that it can handle heavier loads. In load tests, it often appears to be the metal close to the joint that tears while the weld itself remains intact. The surface of pistons or cylinders is often hardened by laser to improve its lifespan. Aircraft engines not treated in this way would have an appreciably lower efficiency and would have to be maintained more regularly. Because of the immense heating of the surface of the metal, the lattice structure of the iron and carbon atoms is compacted and 'frozen' in that state by the rapid cooling after the processing. This results in a smoother and wear-resistant surface. Another advantage of laser-hardening compared with oven-hardening is that when a large part of a surface is heated (as in the latter), there will inevitably be some distortion; this does not occur in laser-hardening. This results in much tighter tolerances.

Many organizations have been using lasers for cutting materials for some time. When steel or titanium has to be cut cleanly, there are only two possible ways of doing so: by laser beam or water jet. The laser makes possible the most accurate contours in any material: paper, plastic film, textiles, cardboard, wooden jigsaw puzzles, tinplate, sawblades, car parts, and so on. In the case of synthetic materials the cut edges are sealed at the same time as the cutting takes place: this makes edging or hemming unnecessary.

In microelectronics, the laser is a gift from heaven. Inscribing ICs, the accurate placing of tracks on a printed-circuit board, the welding of microscopically small terminal leads, the removal of insulation, or the doping of semiconductors – these are all simple with the aid of a laser. Is it therefore surprising that the world's smallest motor, hardly bigger than a grain of wheat, was constructed with the aid of a laser? Designers of printed-circuit boards no longer need to expose, develop and etch their prototypes, but simply place a board under the laser's cutting head and have the laser fabricate the board within a few seconds – including the holes for the electronic parts, of course.

Distances, gas emissions, the thickness of a film of laquer, tiny movements, earth quakes, speeds, velocities or numbers – a laser can measure them all.

If after reading this chapter you still consider the laser a novelty, consider that you probably already own one. If you have a CD player at home or in your car, you have a laser. And after you have read the next chapter, that may not remain the only one.

3. Applications:
experiments and
construction projects

A certain amount of practical experience, preparation, tools, and parts are required for the work described in this chapter. Absolutely indispensable are a good-quality soldering iron, snipe nosed pliers, side cutters, a large and a small cross-head screwdriver, a large and a small standard screwdriver, combination pliers, 60/40 solder 18 SWG, insulated equipment wire (single-strand and multi-strand, both in various colours), an assortment of resistors and capacitors, bolts, nuts and washers of various sizes, and a good-quality multimeter. Useful are an oscilloscope, a function generator, a number of stripboards and breadboards. It is also helpful if you can make your own printed-circuit boards.

3.1 Preparatory work

You will probably remember from your school days what voltage, current and resistance are, but if you have no experience of electronics construction and technology, starting work with practical lasers will not be easy. It is advisable to gain some experience first, which may be acquired by buying and constructing an electronics kit or two, which are available from a number of mail order firms or electronics retailers. Such kits enable you to gain some basic knowledge of electronics construction in a simple yet interesting manner. Do not start with expensive kits, but try the smaller and preferably useful models, which may be handy in the home or in the car. In any case, do not buy a kit just because …

Power supply
For all the construction projects described in this chapter, a good, well regulated power source with variable output and able to provide reasonable

Figure 3-1
Circuit diagram of the
variable power supply

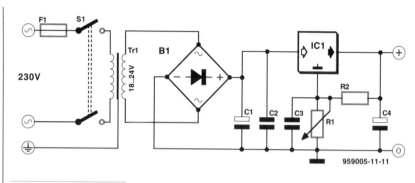

Figure 3-1
Circuit diagram of the
variable power supply

Components list for
Figure 3-1

IC_1 = LM317

R_1 = 5 kΩ potentiometer
R_2 = 220 Ω, metal film, 1%

C_1 = 4700 μF, 35 V, electrolytic
C_2, C_3 = 100 nF, metallized polyester (MKT)
C_4 = 100 μF, 35 V, electrolytic

B_1 = bridge rectifier, B40C3700

Tr_1 = mains transformer, 50 VA, secondary 24 V, 2 A

F_1 = fuse, 1 A, slow

currents is a must. The diagram of a suitable power supply is shown in Figure 3-1. It uses the Type LM317 variable voltage regulator. This integrated circuit, IC_1, can deliver currents of up to 1.5 A and is easy to use. The output voltage is variable between 1.5 V and 22 V. The mains transformer, Tr_1, may be an inexpensive 50 VA model with a 24 V secondary that can provide a current of up to 2 A. The bridge rectifier, B_1, converts this alternating voltage into a pulsating direct voltage of 34 V ($\sqrt{2} \times 24$ V), which is buffered by an electrolytic capacitor, C_1. This gives the LM317 a sufficiently wide control range to regulate the output voltage even at maximum current. The regulator converts the undulating potential across C_1 into a steady direct voltage, whose level is set with variable resistor R_1.

The power supply should be housed in a sturdy metal enclosure. The output voltage is brought out via two 4 mm terminal sockets. Providing the unit with a voltmeter and ammeter (which are available as ready-made panel meters) is very useful, but not essential. However, since the LM317 has no current limiting, an ammeter is not a luxury. If used, it should be connected in series with the circuit earth (−ve terminal of C_4 and the '0' output terminal.

All parts of the metal case must be strapped to the mains earth via a separate screw, nut and serrated washer. DO NOT use one of the fixing screws for this purpose.

In Europe, a mains filter is obligatory and normally this is already provided in the mains inlet, which should be fused. The filter eliminates mains borne radio frequency interference when used with radios, computers or other r.f. sensitive equipment; it also prevents radio frequency interference (RFI) from escaping on to the mains supply.

A power supply unit so constructed is very reliable and, thanks to the isolation between the primary and secondary windings of the transformer and the earthing, also safe to touch. It is, of course, possible to buy a ready-made variable power supply unit from an electronics retailer, but this is rather more expensive. If you do this, however, get one with presettable current limiting. This costs a little more, but it may save expensive, vulnerable components later on.

Regulator for battery-operated power supply

Power supplies for control electronics in lasers are normally regulated and battery operated. The regulator is invariably a low-drop model. Two regulator circuits are standard: one for asymmetric (that is, single) power supplies (Figure 3-2) and the other for symmetric (that is, double) ones (Figure 3-3). The battery is normally a 9 V type, which may be a dry-cell type, but a rechargeable NiCd or NiMH one is strongly recommended. Modern rechargeable types have a capacity of about 110 mAh, which gives many hours of use. If, however, the laser diode is to be supplied by the same battery, it is better to use HP11 (C, R14) or HP2 (D, R20) size batteries, which have a capacity of 1–2 Ah. Note that NiMH batteries do not have the so-called memory effect of NiCd batteries. This effect manifests itself during the charging of not fully discharged NiCd batteries in the formation of gas bubbles between the various layers which cover the surface partly or wholly and degrade the battery capacity. In the long term, this may destroy the battery altogether.

Figure 3-2
Voltage regulator for
battery operation

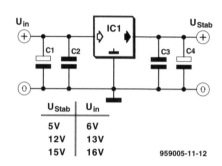

U_{Stab}	U_{in}
5V	6V
12V	13V
15V	16V

959005-11-12

Components list for
Figures 3-2 and 3-3
(Two of each required
for 3.3)

IC_1 = LM2940

C_1 = 2200 μF, 25 V, electrolytic
C_2, C_3 = 100 nF, metallized polyester (MKT)
C_4 = 100 μF, 25 V, electrolytic

The regulator is a low-drop Type LM2940, which is available for output voltages of 5 V, 12 V, and 15 V. The input voltage needs to be only 0.5 V higher than the nominal output voltage to ensure satisfactory operation. The capacitors suppress any tendency to oscillation and also improve the pulse stability. The simple circuit for an asymmetric output voltage is shown in Figure 3-2. The regulator can easily be constructed on a stripboard.

Connecting two of these regulators as shown in Figure 3-3 results in symmetric ($\pm$) output voltages. This is not the most elegant way of getting

Figure 3-3
Combination of two
single power supplies
to obtain symmetric
power lines

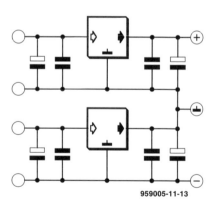

959005-11-13

double supply lines, but it is very simple. Note that this circuit can be used only if the two batteries are electrically isolated.

The advantage of using these circuits lies in the details. For instance, because of the small voltage drop across the regulator (difference between input and output voltages), the dissipation in the IC is small, so that a heat sink is normally not required. Moreover, a larger part of the battery capacity can be utilized since the output voltage remains steady even when the battery voltage has dropped below its nominal value.

Power meter

In an ideal world, it would be simple to just go out and buy a calibrated power meter, but in the real world such an instrument is affordable by only a few. Fortunately, a simple power meter, the diagram of which is shown in Figure 3-4, can be constructed very easily.

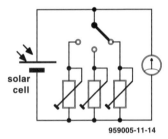

959005-11-14

Figure 3-4
Circuit of a
simple power
measurement unit

The passive instrument is based on an encapsulated solar cell, in front of which a concave lens is mounted. This ensures that a large part of the solar cell is illuminated by even a thin laser beam. The prototype enables measuring powers down to 10 mW with sufficient accuracy. A filter should be used when large powers are being measured.

The solar cell is connected in parallel with a moving coil meter and a series network consisting of a three-position switch and three preset, multi-turn potentiometers. The series network enables three metering ranges to be used. For the calibration a standard power meter or a laser whose output power is accurately known is required. A components list was considered unnecessary.

Figure 3-5
Circuit diagram of the
battery monitor

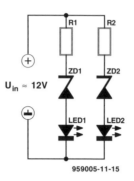

959005-11-15

Components list for
Figure 3-5

LED$_1$ = green
LED$_2$ = red
ZD$_1$ = zener diode, 10 V
ZD$_2$ = zener diode, 13 V

R$_1$ = 680 Ω, carbon or metallized film
R$_2$ = 1.2 kΩ, carbon or metallized film

Battery monitor

A battery monitor is needed to check the state of charge of batteries. The circuit diagram of a fairly simple one is shown in Figure 3-5. Two low-current light-emitting diodes (LEDs) give an indication of the battery voltage, so that an early warning is given of a (nearly) discharged battery. The voltage levels at which the diodes light depend to some extent on the tolerances of the zener diodes, but that does not matter in this application.

If a battery of different nominal voltage is used, zener diodes of different rating must be used. The rating of ZD$_1$ is simply the battery voltage, U$_{in}$, less the forward voltage of the LED$_1$, that is 1.6 V. The rating of ZD$_2$ is U$_{in}$ + 1.6.V. If zener diodes rated at the values so calculated are not available, take the nearest standard value (higher or lower).

In normal circumstances, only LED$_1$ lights to indicate that the battery voltage is within operational limits. The other LED lights only when the voltage is too high and this warning prevents damage to components that cannot tolerate too high a voltage. If neither LED lights, the battery voltage is too low. The battery must then be replaced (if dry) or recharged.

3.2 Wavelength of frequently used lasers

The following table gives an overview of the main data of the most frequently used lasers. The wavelength stated always refers to the strongest or most often used line(s).

Type	Colour	Wavelength (nm)	Applications
Excimer lasers			
argon-fluorine	UV	193	Me_1, I_2, I_{10}
krypton-chlorine	UV	222	
krypton-fluorine	UV	248	
xenon-fluorine	UV	308	Me_2, I_{10}
Gas lasers			
nitrogen	UV	337	R_3, I_6
helium-cadmium	UV	325	R_3, I_6
	violet	441	R_3, I_6
argon	blue	488	C_2, C_7, Me_1, Me_2
	green	514	C_2, C_7, Me_1, Me_2
krypton	blue	476	C_2, C_7
	green	528	C_2, C_7
	yellow	568	C_2, C_7
	red	647	C_2, C_7, Me_1
xenon	white	several	Me_2
helium-neon	green	543	I_1, I_4
	yellow	594	I_1
	orange	612	I_1
	red	633	I_1, I_4, C_1, C_5
	near-IR	1152	R_3
	mid-IR	3390	R_3
hydrogen-fluorine	mid-IR	2700	I_6
carbon-dioxide	far-IR	10 600	I_3, I_8, I_9, Me_2
Metal-vapor lasers			
copper vapour	green	510	Me_6
	yellow	570	Me_6
gold vapour	red	627	Me_6

Table 3.1
Laser types and their wavelength

Type	Colour	Wavelength (nm)	Applications
Solid-state lasers			
Nd:YAG (2f)	green	532	Me_2, C_7, Mi_2
Nd:YAG	near-IR	1064	I_7, I_8, I_{10}, Me_2
erbium-glass	mid-IR	1540	R_3
erbium-YAG	mid-IR	2940	Me_2. Me_3
holmium:YLF	mid-IR	2060	R_3
holmium:YAG	mid-IR	2100	Me_2, Me_3
ruby	red	694	Me_2, Me_6
alexandrite	near-IR	700–815	R_3
Dye lasers			
rhodamine 6G	VIS	570–650	Me_1, Me_2
coumarone C30	green	504	Me_2
Semiconductor lasers			
gallium-arsenide (GaAs)	near-IR	840	C_3, C_5, C_8
gallium-aluminium-arsenide	far-IR/near-IR	635–830	C_1, C_2, C_3

Abbreviations:

UV	ultraviolet	200–400 nm
VIS	visible	400–700 nm
near-IR (IR-A)	near-infra-red	700–1400 nm
mid-IR (IR-B)	mid-infra-red	1400–3000 nm
far-IR (IR-C)	far-infra-red	3000 nm–1 mm

C	commercial
I	industrial
Me	medical
Mi	military
R	research

Industrial applications
1 measurement technology
2 temper-hardening

Commercial applications
1 copying machines
2 displays

Table 3.1
Laser types (cont'd)

Industrial applications (cont'd)

3   sawing/drilling
4   dynamic balancing
5   metrology
6   non-destructive testing
7   sealing
8   soldering/smelting
9   materials processing
10 lithography
11 construction
12 spectroscopy

Medical applications
1   eye surgery (ophthalmology)
2   general surgery
3   dentistry
4   diagnostics
5   genetic research
6   plastic surgery

Research applications
1   interferometry
2   nuclear fusion research
3   spectroscopy
4   speed/velocity measurement

Commercial applications (cont'd)

3   communications
4   holography
5   printers
6   scanners
7   light shows
8   compact/video disks

Military applications
1   navigation
2   distance measurement
3   simulation
4   weaponry
5   homing systems
6   illumination

3.3 Safety regulations

Although this is not the place to have pages and pages full of safety regulations, laws, ordinances, and other provisions, some have to be stated.

Readers interested in the full details should obtain NEN Norm 60825 from the British Standards Institute or their own country's Standards Authority.

The dangers inherent in a beam of laser light must not be underestimated. Even the light from a laser with a power of only a few milliwatts is dangerous for the human eye. The light emitted by a laser of one milliwatt

59

is more intense than direct sunlight! Light from a 100 mW laser can cause serious burns. It is, therefore, imperative to stick to the rules and regulations governing lasers. Apart from the laser light itself, there are other life-threatening dangers associated with laser systems. For instance, in case of a large He-Ne laser, the voltage across the terminals is a few thousand volts at a current level of a few milliwatts. You will probably not be able to recount the experience when you touch these terminals.

Very large currents flow in water-cooled argon or mixed-gas lasers. If you drop a screwdriver between the anode and the casing, it will probably evaporate. To give you an idea of the danger of such currents: they are of the same level as those used for welding.

The relevant regulations leave no doubt as to how one should treat lasers and why. However, all regulations – and there are a great many – must be interpreted in a practical manner. In most regulations, you frequently meet the words 'should' or 'ought to' and these indicate a certain leeway. Large organizations employ a safety inspector to ensure that the necessary rules and regulations are observed – in a practical manner.

When you have to set up a laser, take off all pieces of jewelry, rings, watches, nechlaces, tie-pins, and so on. These are prime sources of danger as far as reflections are concerned and therefore absolutely not permitted. When working on lasers with powers greater than 10 mW, safety glasses must be worn – make sure when you buy these that they also give full sideways protection. Unfortunately, these cannot be worn when adjusting a laser, because you cannot see the laser beam; for this purpose, there are special glasses.

In most western countries, the law unambiguously states that a system containing a laser of Class 3 and higher must be reported to, and licensed by, the Health and Safety Inspectorate if it is to be used in a public place for whatever purpose. This means that if you start a company or a workshop that is open to persons other than yourself, that is, your employees or customers, and you have a laser Class 3 or higher, you must obtain a license before you can take the laser into use. This is, for instance, of importance, in case of a laser show in a discotheque. Note that it is you, the owner of the laser equipment who is responsible in law for the licensing, not the person to whom you have rented it for an evening or the person who hires out the hall for the laser show. Note that if something goes wrong with the equipment in a public place or you are found not to have a license, the equipment may be confiscated.

However, if you as a private person use a laser in your own home or garage (as long as unauthorized people have no access) you may do with it what you wish, as long as it does not harm life or property of third parties.

Insurance
If you are an employer, you have, of course, the necessary insurance(s) to cover your liabilities. Beware, however, because most policies explicitly exclude any damage, direct or indirect, caused by laser beams. You must, therefore, make absolutely certain that a relevant clause regarding liability for such damage is included. Many people are not aware of the exclusion.

3.4 Eavesdropping equipment

Ever since the invention of the wireless, people have used radio equipment to listen to conversations not intended for their ears. During the Cold War years, this occupation was a commonplace for any self-respecting spy or informer. In the early days, tiny long-wave radio transmitters were built into the receiver of a telephone and their radiation picked up at a not-too-distance location. Later, mini and micro transmitters operating in the very-high frequency (VHF) band were used, which required far less power than the early devices. Famous examples can be seen in many films; a particular one is in a James Bond film, in which an olive functioned as the transmitter and a cocktail stick as the antenna. What would have happened if anyone had eaten the olive is anybody's guess. There were also necktie microphones, which were countered by interference transmitters. The general and big drawback of all these apparatus was that the transmissions could be received by any broadband receiver and by unauthorized persons. To some extent this was prevented by the use of directional microphones and parabolic reflectors to beam the sound, but these were hardly inconspicuous.

Lasers gave these activities a new lease of life. Since laser diodes are easily available and inexpensive, it is a simple matter to build an eavesdropping unit, even if you are not interested in the domestic quibbles of your neighbours. The interesting principle of the project is reason enough to build it. Remember, however, that intrusion of privacy is always asocial and often illegal.

The principle

The principle of the equipment is very simple indeed. It is well known that in any conversation sound waves are produced that are propagated through the air. The speed of sound waves at sea level is almost exactly 333 m/s or 1200 km/h. When sound waves collide with an object this will begin to vibrate, however slightly, more or less in rhythm with the modulation and frequencies of the waves. More or less, because although in theory it should be exactly, in practice there are external factors to be considered such as absorption of the sound energy and resonance phenomena in the object that is hit. These factors cause distortion. But, never mind: when the sound waves hit an object at one side, the object begins to vibrate and imparts the vibration, including any distortion, back to the air at the other side. It is these latter vibrations that we need. This is, perhaps, best explained with reference to a window. Readers are, no doubt, aware that conversations and other sounds in a room can be heard, perhaps faintly, even through a closed window. The type of glass in the window pane and the loudness of the voices or sounds determine the volume of the sound at the other side of the window. But even when a good isolating kind of glass (double glazing) is used, we can hear the voices quite well when we press our ear against the window pane. This means that what we need is an extension of our ear.

The simplest extension is, of course, a microphone. Attached to the window pane, it picks up the sounds and vibrations inside the room and these can be reproduced elsewhere after they have been amplified. Microphones are visible, however, and, therefore, easily detected by inspection. So, what else can we do?

Solution

Take a laser beam, direct it at a certain angle on to a window, pick up the reflected beam with a suitable detector, and listen. In practice, it is just as simple as it is written here. With the use of a well-focused laser diode, a narrow laser beam is directed on to a window. The glass in the window reflects at least part of the beam in a direction depending on the angle of incidence. When the glass in the window is set into vibration, the reflected laser beam vibrates in rhythm, so that the detector can follow the original vibrations exactly. But, be careful: the glass will also pass part of the laser beam. So, the use of an He-Ne laser in the visible spectrum would be rather too conspicuous. Therefore, an invisible beam must be used. There

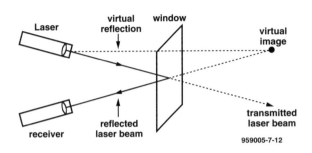

Laser
virtual reflection
window
virtual image
receiver
reflected laser beam
transmitted laser beam
959005-7-12

Figure 3-6
When laser and receiver are at the correct angle with respect to one another, the performance of the system is optimum.

is another little problem: since the angle of incidence of the beam must be close to, but not quite, 90°, we need a location more or less opposite the window in question to be able to set up our equipment correctly.

The circuit

The circuit, whose diagram is shown in Figure 3-7, has been specially designed for this purpose. Special circuit techniques and components ensure excellent performance. The five transistors used guarantee highly satisfactory operation with great sensitivity. The photo transistor detects the reflected and modulated laser beam and applies its output signal to the following filter and amplifier stages. Note the capacitive coupling of the amplifier stages. We have deliberately not used direct coupling since we do not want any low-frequency interference. In particular, the value of C_4 is such that mains interference is largely filtered out. The value of this capacitor may be slightly lower if you still suffer from mains interference.

You may ask why the circuit has been designed from discrete components. The answer to this is that (a) it is easier to clone, and (b) it may be modified more readily for special applications. The earth connections are rather critical. To avoid oscillations or interference, they need to be star-shaped. The result is well worth the additional work.

The input stages are designed to give an amplification of × 40; the driver stage amplifies ×10. A crystal earpiece can be connected directly to the output provided it has an impedance of not less than 1 kΩ. If this is not the case, an impedance transformer must be used. If desired, an external amplifier can be linked to jumper JP_1.

The circuit draws power from a 9 V dry or rechargeable battery. Connections to the potentiometer and switch must be made in twisted or preferably screened wire. If screened wire is used, the screen should be

Figure 3-7
Circuit diagram of the
eavesdropping
receiver

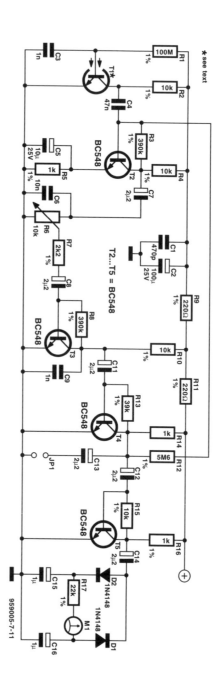

Components list for
Figure 3-7

R_1 = 100 MΩ
R_2, R_4, R_{10}, R_{15} = 10 kΩ*
R_3, R_8 = 390 kΩ*
R_5, R_{14}, R_{16} = 1 kΩ*
R_6 = 10 kΩ, potentimeter with switch
R_7 = 2.2 kΩ*
R_{12} = 5.6 MΩ*
R_{13} = 39 kΩ*
R_{17} = 22 kΩ*
R_9, R_{11} = 220 Ω*
• 1%, metal film

C_1 = 470 pF, disc
C_2 = 100 μF, 25 V, electrolytic
C_3, C_9 = 1 nF, disc
C_4 = 47 nF, metallized polyester (MKT)
C_5 = 10 μF, 25 V, electrolytic
C_6 = 10 nF, ceramic
C_7, C_8, C_{11}–C_{14} = 2.2 μF, tantalum
C_{15}, C_{16} = 1 μF, tantalum

T_1 = photo transistor, various types are suitable
T_2–T_5 = general-purpose transistor such as BC548
D_1, D_2 = 1N4148

earthed at one end only.

Construction

The circuit is best housed in a cylindrical enclosure such as a piece of PVC tubing together with the lens for the photo transistor. For convenience of handling, a second, thinner, piece of PVC tube may be glued at right angles to the enclosure. This 'handle' may be used to house the battery, together with a connector for a battery charger if a rechargeable battery is used.

The laser is mounted in parallel with the main enclosure and must be optically well adjusted. If an infra-red laser is used, an IR filter is needed to prevent interference by ambient light. The range of the laser may be increased appreciably by the use of a large lens with an equally large focal length. The directivity of the unit is in direct proportion to the length of the receiver tube, since a long tube eliminates most sideway interference.

Comments
The optical receiver is of interest also without the use of a laser, since it can be used for the detection of all kinds of light signal. For instance, in conjunction with a frequency meter, it can measure the repetition rate of (multiplexed) displays, television receivers and other equipment.

If an infra-red laser is used, an IR filter in the receiver is indispensable, because this prevents ambient visible light from falling on to the photo transistor so that this does not get overdriven. The filter therefore improves the performance of the receiver appreciably, even more so in conjunction with a large lens.

The sound quality may be improved with the aid of a graphic equalizer at the output of the receiver, since this enables spurious resonances or interference frequencies to be filtered out. There is no clear method for doing this: experimenting is the only way.

The angles between the laser and receiver and the window need not be equal as drawn in Figure 3-6 to pick up any vibrations. Particularly when an IR laser is used, diffusion may be sufficient to eavesdrop at a wider angle, but only over short distances.

3.5 Alarm system

There are various ways of constructing an alarm system based on a laser. Large areas and gardens, long corridors or large windows can be guarded effectively by a laser. What's more, burglars and other unwanted intruders do not even get the opportunity of disabling the system by switching off the mains.

In all this, it must not be forgotten that large laser powers are dangerous for the eyes not only of the intruder but also of the rightful owner of the property. Unfortunately, you cannot simply claim that the burglar should not have broken in to commit a nefarious act. If such a person would sustain an eye injury through the laser light, you are fully responsible; it does not matter whether the culprit was vandalizing your home or about to be off with some of your belongings (who denied that the law is an ass?).

Strict adherence to the law would even require warning notices that such a system was in operation. Whatever, in such a system only a Class 2 laser with a power output not exceeding 1 milliwatt is allowed.

The word laser in itself is enough to fire the imagination of many people. Laymen often have the weirdest ideas of the nature of a laser alarm system. Some think that it is a system to blind burglars if not permanently than for a short time, long enough to get such a wicked person to the nearest police station. Others think that it is a homing beam that remains pointed at the intruder, or a cutting torch to brand the burglar. Technically, all these would be perfectly possible, but they are illegal.

However, let us revert to an impressive, well-functioning alarm system. Almost without exception, such a system is based on one and the same principle: that of beam interruption. The effectiveness of the system is therefore primarily dependent on the ingenious path of the laser beam. The reliability can be improved by the use of an infra-red laser. In such a system, a narrow-band filter limits interference by ambient light. Moreover, the burglar cannot see the beam. On the other hand, setting up and adjusting an IR beam is fairly tedious, particularly when long(ish) distances are involved. An additional lens system in front of the laser holds the beam focused over long distances.

Protecting a building
Owing to the large distances to be spanned in protecting a building, the path of the beam around it must not be too complex. Bear in mind also that the laser light is attenuated by dust particles in the air or by mist or fog; when such attenuation is serious, it may give rise to a false alarm. This may be obviated by modulating the laser light with a high-frequency signal, say, 100 kHz.

The detector is the receiver described in Section 3.13. In this case, instead of a loudspeaker a band-pass filter is connected to the output of the receiver. The centre frequency of this filter is equal to the modulating frequency, that is, 100 kHz. A trigger circuit connected to the output of the filter actuates the alarm proper. This circuit may be based on a relay that is tripped in the quiescent state: it would thus set off the alarm when the supply lines are broken. It is a good idea to use a lead-acid battery as a standby supply in case the normal supply lines fall out. If these supply lines are 13.8 V, they may also serve to keep the battery charged at all times. Note that a potential of 13.8 V is just below that of a fully charged lead-

Figure 3-8
Possible layout of a
guard system for a
building in its own
grounds

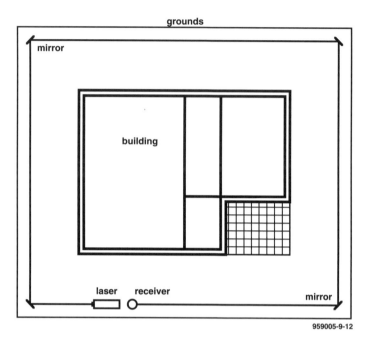

959005-9-12

acid battery, so that overcharging cannot take place. Depending on the capacity of the battery, it can power the system for a couple of days. When the breaks in normal supply are shorter, nickel-metal-hydride (NiMH) batteries may be used. Since the current drawn by the alarm system is small, these batteries, which are not affected by the memory effect, are perfectly adequate in most cases.

A building can simply be given an invisible fence that immediately signals the presence of an intruder. Unfortunately, we must take account of the fact that some of the more intelligent of these criminals are aware of modern technologies.

A little thought quickly shows that a single beam around a building cannot give adequate protection. More effective and more reliable methods, not exclusively based on lasers, are available for this. Nevertheless, the basic principle of such system remains the same. A corridor, for instance, may be equipped with a laser and a number of mirrors as shown in Figure 3-9. In this way, a network of light beams is formed ending in an optical detector.

An even more effective method is scanning the object to be protected.

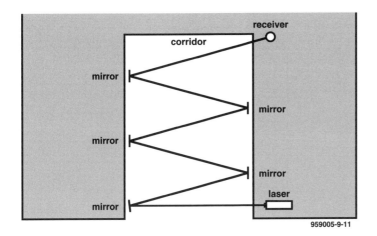

Figure 3-9
Guarding a
corridor with a laser
beam network

If, for instance, a valuable object is to be protected, it can be scanned continuously by a laser beam. The pattern of the scan needs to be input only once and is then compared with the mosr recent scan. The slightest difference will cause the alarm to be set off.

The object is regularly scanned with the aid of an open-scan system according to a fixed pattern.After each change of direction of the beam, the reflected signal is measured by a photo transistor and compared with the 'learned' value. When the measured value corresponds to the learned value (within certain limits), the beam is directed on to the next position. If the measured value does not correspond, the remaining positions are scanned and when a preset number of measuring positions does not correspond with the learned value, the alarm is actuated. The likelihood of a false alarm is infinitesimal.

Very impressive and very effective is the operation of a laser alarm system based on a gyroscope as shown in Figure 3-10. In this system a small laser is affixed to the object to be guarded or on the base on which it stands. The laser beam is guided around and over the object via a beam splitter. The resulting beams are output to external sensors.

Operation of the system is as follows. When the base on which the object is placed, or the object itself, is moved in the slightest, the laser beams will not fall on to the mirror, whereupon the alarm is actuated. The system may be made even more sensitive by not affixing the laser to the object or its base, but placing it externally and directing its beam on to the object via mirrors. Even the slightest movement of the object causes the beams to fall outside the sensors, whereupon the alarm is set off.

Figure 3-10
Laser alarm system
based on gyroscope
principle

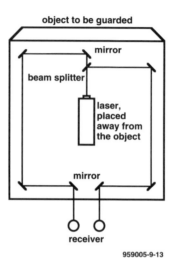

As we have seen, an alarm system based on a laser can be very effective and has a number of advantages over conventional protection systems. However, never lose sight of the fact that such a laser (which in law is considered to be in a public place) must be limited to a Class 2 model, which means that its output must not exceed 1 milliwatt. It is, of course, possible to use a higher output, but you then need a suitable license. Bear in mind at all times that you as the owner of the system are responsible at all times for any injury sustained by another person, even if that person was in your premises illegally.

3.6 Distance meter

The distance meter described is something special: in an ultra-modern manner, the time lapse between the instant a beam of light is emitted by a laser diode and the instant a photo transistor detects the reflected light is used to determine the distance to the target with surprising precision. You may ask, since the measurement of elapsed times is known to be notoriously difficult, how a simple circuit as shown in Figure 3-12 can carry out such amazingly accurate measurements. The answer is that the distances measured with the circuit are limited to about 20 metres, so that a single laser pulse is sufficient to carry out a measurement. In other words, we

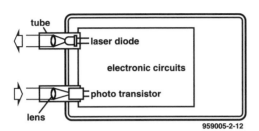

tube
laser diode
electronic circuits
photo transistor
lens
959005-2-12

Figure 3-11
Principle of
distance
measurement

know that the pulse detected by the photo transistor is definitely the one emitted by the laser and not a spurious one.

The laser diode is controlled by an oscillator that generates very short pulses. At the instant that a pulse is generated, an analogue time measurement is commenced and this is stopped again when the reflected pulse reaches the photo transistor. In other words, the laser diode, sender and receiver form a sort of oscillatory circuit whose frequency is determined by the distance. So, the result of the measurement is a frequency that is applied to a mechanical moving coil meter which, owing to its inertia, indicates an average value. The various preset potentiometers serve to set the sensitivity, calibrate the circuit, and adapt the circuit to ambient conditions. Provided the circuit is built with the necessary care and precision, distances of up to 20 metres can be measured accurately and reliably.

Construction

The circuit in Figure 3-12 may be built on a stripboard. Although the usual care and attention must be paid to the constructional details, the circuit is very easy to build. The laser diode and photo transistor, together with an appropriate lens to collimate the light, are each housed in a long tube (Figure 3-11). The range of the meter will depend strongly on the correct choice of focal length. The tubes are mounted side by side and connected by the shortest possible wires to the circuit on the stripboard.

The symmetrical power supply provides an output of ±4.5 V. It may consist of eight HP11 (C, R11) dry or rechargeable batteries in series with the earth connection to the junction of the 4th and 5th batteries, which would produce ±4.8 V. It is also possible to use two 9 V batteries in series, again centre-tapped, followed by a Type 7805 regulator in the +ve line and a Type 7905 in the −ve line. There is no great price difference between the two arrangements, but that using 9 V batteries has the advan-

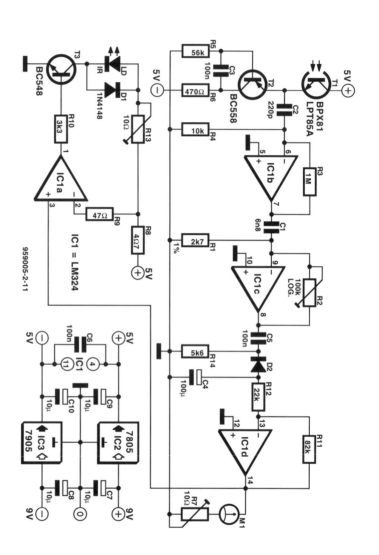

Figure 3-12
Circuit diagram of the
distance meter

R_1 = 2.7 kΩ, metal film, 1%
R_2 = 100 kΩ, multiturn preset potentiometer
R_3 = 1 MΩ
R_4 = 10 kΩ
R_5 = 56 kΩ
R_6 = 470 Ω
R_7, R_{13} = 10 Ω, multiturn preset potentiometer
R_8 = 4.7 Ω
R_9 = 47 Ω
R_{10} = 3.3 kΩ
R_{11} = 82 kΩ
R_{12} = 22 kΩ
R_{14} = 5.6 kΩ

C_1 = 0.068 μF
C_2 = 220 pF
C_3, C_5, C_6 = 0.001 μF
C_4 = 100 μF, electrolytic

LD = LTO22MC (IR laser diode, 780 nm)
D_1 = 1N4148
T_1 = BPX81
T_2 = BC558 or equivalent
T_3 = BC548 or equivalent

IC_1 = LM324

M_1 = moving coil meter 1V f.s.d.

Components list for Figure 3-12 (excluding power supply)

tage that the calibration remains fixed since the supply lines remain stable.

The entire meter may be housed in a small, hand-held enclosure, of which a variety is available from mail-order firms and electronics retailers. After the construction has been completed, the circuit must be calibrated with the aid of the preset potentiometers. This can, of course, only be done with a suitable tape measure.

3.7 Laser light transmission via optical fibre

As we have seen earlier, laser light is almost ideally suited for transmission via an optical fibre. And this does not refer just to data transmission but to real power tranmission. This section describes an experiment with an He-Ne laser for which is needed:

- 5 mW He-Ne laser with thun beam;
- 2 off achromatic lens – f = 20 mm;
- 1 off achromatic lens – f = 16 mm;
- a length of optical fibre, core diameter 100 μm;
- wet and dry sandpaper, no. 600 (very fine)
- lens holders as appropriate;
- holders adjustable in the X- and Y-planes;
- a small strip of tin plate

Since optical fibres are very easily damaged, no guarantees can be given as to a successful result of this experiment. Also, optical fibre in short lengths is not that easily obtained. Moreover, it is very difficult to polish the ends of an optical fibre to a smoothness that ensures correct connection between it and the laser beam. You will almost certainly have to have a few tries before you are even moderately successful, but ... practice makes perfect. Do not expect professional results in a short time. Also, do not use a high-power laser as this may well damage the optical fibre. If you are lucky, however, you may well be able to obtain a length of optical cable with polished ends. This forms only the beginning, however: there are a few other matters to be considered. But let us first look at the construction of the optical fibre system.

It will be assumed that you have an unbroken, non-polished and non-processed length of optical fibre that you want to prepare for use. Place the very fine sandpaper on a flat surface and start to polish the end of the fibre, complete with the cladding by gently moving it across the emery paper. Take great care to hold the fibre at right angles to the sandpaper so as to obtain a flat surface. This operation is facilitated by a small block of wood in which a hole with the same diameter as the fibre is drilled at right angles to one plane. Insert the fibre into this hole and polish. In this way you can be sure that the fibre is at right angles to the sandpaper—see Figure 3-13. Continue until you judge by sight that the end is flat and smooth. Dampen the sandpaper and repeat the entire operation.

You may rest assured that your first attempts will be failures. This is quite normal and no reason to start doubting your skills. When you are finally successful, repeat the process with the other end of the fibre. When you are satisfied with this, the next step can be taken.

Using a sharp knife, remove the cladding from the fibre ends. This has to be done very carefully so as not to damage the core. Screw the fibre to the adjustable holder with the aid of the strip of tin plate in such a way that

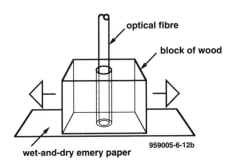

*Figure 3-13
Simple aid for
polishing the end of
an optical fibre*

1–2 mm protrudes from it.

Switch on the laser and mark the spot where the light beam hits the wall; leave the laser as it is. Fix one of the 20 mm achromatic lenses in a sturdy lens-holder and put this in front of the laser. Position the lens so that the centre of the divergent beam is exactly at the spot you have marked previously—see Figure 3-14.

Arrange the system roughly as shown in Figure 3-15. Move the end of the optical fibre (in the adjustable holder) to coincide exactly with the focus of the achromatic lens. Depending on the divergence and the diameter of the laser beam, the spot where the laser beam is focused may not exactly coincide with the focus of the lens. Point the other end of the fibre at a white surface, so that you can see from the reflection how the laser beam is coupled to the fibre. Using the fine adjustment of the holder, move the end of the fibre to the focus of the lens. At that moment you will notice the other end of the fibre lighting very brightly to indicate that you have located the focus. Then move the lens to and fro along its optical axis until the coupling is optimal, that is, when the non-focused output beam shows least divergence. The bright spot at the centre is always surrounded by a

Figure 3-14
Step 1 in aligning the
input coupling

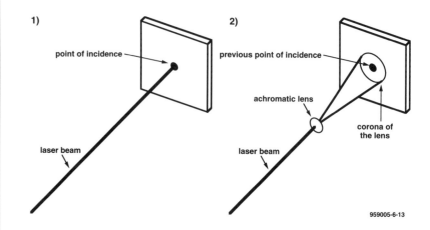

Figure 3-14
Step 1 in aligning the
input coupling

faint corona. You will notice that this spot is considerably brighter than when the laser beam falls on to the wall directly, that is, without the intervention of the optical fibre. This is because the beam on emerging from the fibre consists of a variety of modi.

Next, arrange the second 20 mm achromatic lens at the other end of the fibre—see Figure 3-16. The divergence of the emerging laser beam is controlled by shifting this lens to and fro. Depending on the lens used, the beam will become narrower, but the divergence larger, or vice versa. When the beam has to span fairly long distances (within the specification), it is best to use a lens with a large focal length (up to 50 mm); for short distances, a focal length of 16 mm or not more than 20 mm should be used.

Figure 3-15
Diagram of the input
coupling and the
fixing of the fibre
cable

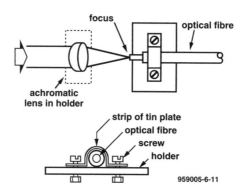

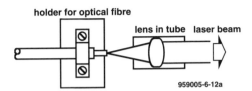

holder for optical fibre

lens in tube   laser beam

959005-6-12a

If the light-spot is not nicely round and crisp, one or both of the ends of the fibre have not been polished properly. In that case, it or they will have to be polished again – try one end first. Couple the laser to the repolished end: hopefully, the result is an improvement. To avoid any misunderstanding, it must be emphasized that the present optical fibre system, owing to the not perfectly polished ends of the fibre, will never perform as well as one using a professionally polished fibre. No matter how hard you have tried, you will not get the quality of a professionally polished fibre. Because of this, the present system must not be used with high-power lasers. Also, it is not comparable for power transmission purposes with a optical fibre system using professional couplings.

The photograph in Figure 3-17 shows a professional optical fibre system. It consists of a coupling with a lens system that can be adjusted in three directions (an achromatic lens consisting of three elements is used), an inlet for an optical fibre with a standard SMA socket, the optical fibre itself (length 10–100 m and a core diameter of 50 μm), and the optics for focusing the emerging beam. It has a price tag of about £1000 (1997) and is therefore not suitable for amateur experiments. The power that can be transmitted by this system may be up to 15 watts depending on the kind of optical fibre used. As the power increases, the losses in the system also increase. The divergence of the emerging laser beam varies with the diameter of the optical fibre, but that is true also of the power losses and the vulnerability of the system as a whole.

3.8 Pulse counter

In this section the building of a number of light barriers will be discussed which are useful for domestic purposes. An example is a lap counter for a model racing circuit. Once you have used this, you will realize what a technically inferior unit a mechanical lap counter is. Of course, it is not

Figure 3-17
Professional optical
fibre system

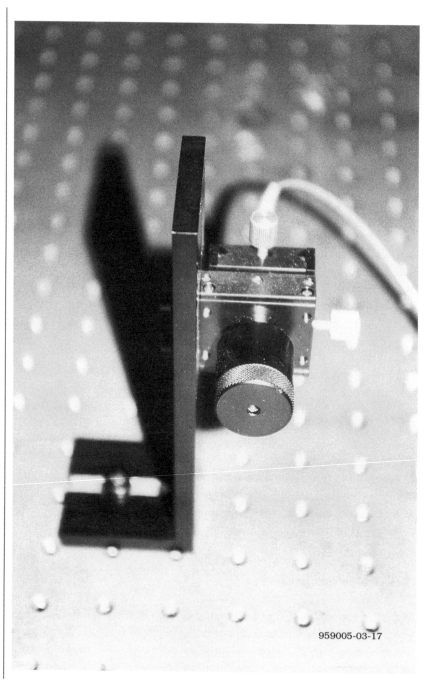

959005-03-17

necessary to use a laser for this, since it can also be built around standard LEDs. But, since this is a book about lasers, ...

The counter could be designed to:

• count by means of light beam interruption;
• count with the aid of a reflected laser beam;
• count by scanning.

The first method (see Figure 3-18) is a non-starter. It is a simple and inexpensive method, since only one sender (A, the laser diode module described elsewhere in this book), one receiver (B) and a counter circuit are needed. It has the serious drawback, however, that cars passing the light barrier in opposite directions break the light beam also and thus increases

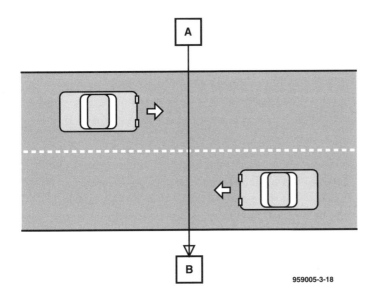

Figure 3-18
Arrangement of the
light barrier for beam
interruption

959005-3-18

the count.

The second method is rather more complex and more expensive, but works immeasurably better (see Figure 3-19). Each track is given its own sender (A) and receiver and counter circuit (B). In the construction, care must obviously be taken to ensure that each of the light beams can be detected only by its 'own' receiver.

The third method is, from a technical point of view, the most challenging, but, owing to the space it requires, its practical construction presents a

Figure 3-19
Arrangement of the
counter circuit on the
reflection principle

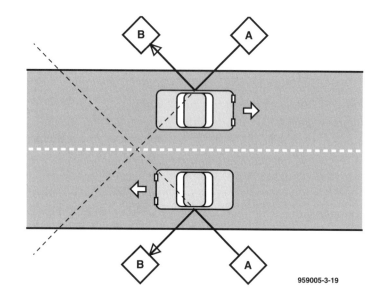

959005-3-19

few problems.

The principle
It is not difficult to detect a reflected laser beam in a system consisting of a sender (the laser diode module described in section 3.9) and a receiver with counter circuit. A model race track has the advantage that the track itself is normally mat black, whereas the cars are finished in a shiny varnish or shellac. It is not necessary to mount the sensors above the tracks on overhangs or bridges; they must, however, be placed at the correct distance from the track. If the laser and the associated receiver are at an angle to the track, a count pulse is generated only when a reflecting object passes the sender at a given distance.

Components list for
Figure 3-20

R_1–R_{10} = 1 kΩ, 1%, metal film

C_1 = 0.001–0.01 μF (the exact value has to be determined empirically)

T_1–T_3 = general-purpose transistor, e.g., BC557

IC_1 = 4553
IC_2 = 4511

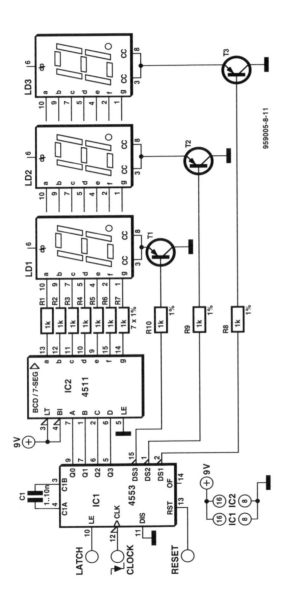

959005-8-11

Figure 3-20.
To ensure reliable
operation, the clock
input of IC$_1$ (pin 12)
should be provided
with a 10 kΩ pull-up
resistor.

The circuit

The design is simple: just as in a mechanical lap counter, each passing car generates one count pulse, which is applied to the counter circuit. It would have been possible to use a mechanical counter with reset facility which, in truth, would have been the simplest and least expensive possibility. However, it was felt that the present counter justifies something a bit different. So, the counter circuit (Figure 3-20) consists of an integrated CMOS circuit, IC_1, a 7-segment decoder, IC_2, and three LED displays. The maximum counter state is 999, more than adequate for an exciting race. Bear in mind that each track requires a counter circuit.

The reaction speed of the counter is set with C_1. This is an important aspect, because brightness variations occurring when a car passes may cause several count pulses (comparable to the bounce of a mechanical switch), and this, of course, is not what is wanted.

Any 7-segment display with common cathode may be used for the overall display. If low-current types are used, the value of resistors R_1–R_7 must be increased to 2.2–2.7 kΩ.

The circuit of the detector of the counter circuit is shown in Figure 3-21. It consists of a photo transistor with collector resistor and a capacitor. The light beam emitted by the laser diode module (Section 3.9) is reflected by a passing racing car. The reflected light falls on to the photo transistor, which causes the clock input of the counter to briefly become low: the counter reading is then increased by one.

When a new race is started, the reading can be reset to 000 with a reset switch as shown in Figure 3-22.

Figure 3-21
The optical detector
of the counter circuit

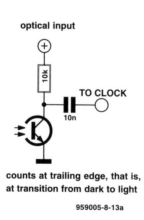

optical input

10k

TO CLOCK

10n

counts at trailing edge, that is,
at transition from dark to light

959005-8-13a

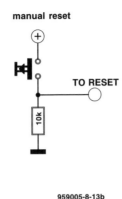

manual reset

TO RESET

10k

959005-8-13b

Figure 3-22
Reset circuit

The supply voltage in the prototype is 9 V, but a lower one of 6 V may also be used. In the latter case, the value of the series resistors of the LEDs must be altered as appropriate.

Frequency/rev counter
Extending the lap counter with a constant time base (see Figure 3-23) converts the lap counter into a frequency meter which counts light pulses during an accurately determined, fixed period of time. The constant time base (1 second or 10 seconds) is provided by a crystal oscillator. During a count period, the circuit counts the incident light pulses, whereupon the result is displayed and the counter is automatically reset. The reading shows the number of pulses per unit of time: in case of a time base (count period) of 1 s, this is the frequency in Hz, and when the time base is 10 s, it is the frequency divided by 10. In conjunction with a laser reflector light barrier, the circuit may be used as a rev counter for model prop aircraft.

The circuit
The circuit shown in Figure 3-23 is based on clock generator X_1. The clock signal is divided by 2 in D-bistable IC_{1a} and then applied to the input of counter IC_2. The output of the counter (at pin 3) is a signal with a period of 1 s; decade scaler IC_3 provides a clock signal of 0.1 s. Either of these clock signals is selected with S_1 and applied to IC_{5a} via D-bistable IC_{1b} (like IC_{1a}, a binary scaler) to gate IC_{5a}.
The receiver of Figure 3-21 is connected to the INPUT terminal. The count pulses generated by the detector are applied to the CLOCK input of

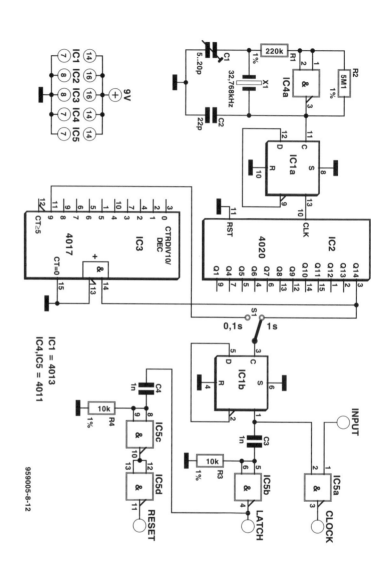

Figure 3-23
Time base circuit for
converting the pulse
counter into a
frequency meter or
revolution counter

Components list for Figure 3-23

R_1 = 220 kΩ*
R_2 = 5.1 MΩ*
R_3, R_4 = 10 kΩ*
* = 1%, metal film

C_1 = 5–20 pF trimmer capacitor
C_2 = 22 pF
C_3, C_4 = 0.001 μF metallized polyester (MKT)

IC_1 = 4013
IC_2 = 4020
IC_3 = 4017
IC_4, IC_5 = 4011

X_1 = crystal, 32.768 kHz

the counter circuit. After the count period has elapsed, a reset signal is generated which causes the counter to be reset to 000. A split second before this, a LATCH signal is generated, which arranges for the counter reading to be stored in a latch and to be displayed. After the next count period has elapsed, the displayed value is refreshed.

Both circuits, that is, the lap counter and the frequency/rev counter adaptor, may be built on a piece of stripboard. During soldering, be careful with the CMOS ICs, since these are very sensitive to static electricity. It is, therefore, advisable to use sockets for these circuits.

3.9 Laser diode module

The laser diode module described in this section is of a quality that merits the prefex 'industrial'. It is constructed with surface-mount devices (SMDs), which in practical use has proved highly reliable. The prototype was tested with a Hitachi Type 6411 and Toshiba Type 9215 and 9211 laser diodes. As you will see, a circuit need not be complex to be of high quality.

Construction

The mechanical construction of electronics, laser diode and collimator lens

Figure 3-24
Construction of the
laser diode module

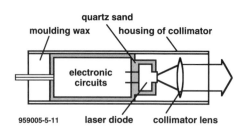

is shown in Figure 3-24.

Before the assembly is fitted, its correct operation needs to be checked with a dummy load at various stages:

- after the circuit has been completed;
- after the laser diode has been fitted;
- after the electronics and laser diode together with the collimator lens have been fitted in the enclosure;
- after the assembly has been secured in position with moulding resin.

When each of these checks is successful, you have not only shown your skill, but you have also been fortunate. Normally, several attempts at each of the stages is needed before everything is in good working order. Usually, some laser diodes give up the ghost in the process. Nevertheless, the construction is not complicated. The laser diode and electronic assembly are pushed into the enclosure which already contains the collimator lens. Then, the enclosure is filled to just above the electronic assembly with very fine sand: shake the whole so that the sand is densely packed. This process reduces the risk of the laser diode moving during the setting of the resin.

Circuit description

The circuit diagram is shown in Figure 3.25. The laser diode, LD_1, operates in the automatic-current control (ACC) mode. This means that the internal monitor diode is not used for two good reasons.

1. The monitor diode, which is integrated in the casing of the laser diode, measures the optical output power and adjusts this with the aid of an external control circuit if needed. So, in case of an automatic power control (APC) drive with monitor diode connected, the output power of the diode is always being adjusted. This means that the current through the diode is not constant. In unfavourable operating conditions it may happen that the diode emits insufficient light. The monitor diode in-

creases the current through the diode so as to obtain equilibrium. This means, however, that the laser diode in certain circumstances may be destroyed by a sustained large supply current. This is normally prevented by external current limiting.

2. Monitor diodes usually react very rapidly, so that the APC drive may remove any amplitude modulation. This means, however, that the laser diode cannot be modulated. True, this difficulty may be obviated with the aid of a comparator, by which a second control loop becomes active within the control loop for the output power. This arrangement would make the circuit needlessly more complicated.

All this means that the ACC circuit in Figure 3-25, although simple, serves the present purpose nicely: its reliability has been proved in many hours of operation.

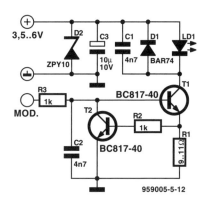

Figure 3-25
Circuit diagram of the automatic current control (ACC)

R_1 = 9–11 Ω, depending on LD_1
R_2, R_3 = 1 kΩ, SMD

C_1, C_2 = 0.0047 μF, SMD
C_3 = 10 μF, 10 V, tantalum

D_1, = BAR74 or equivalent
D_2 = zener, 5 V, 500 mW, e.g., Type ZPY10
T_1, T_2 = BC817-40
LD_1 = laser diode to personal choice

Components list for Figure 3-25

87

Diode D_1, in anti-parallel with the laser diode, provides a simple but effective protection against connecting the supply lines with wrong polarity. Should this occur for a brief moment, no harm is done. If, however, the wrong polarity is retained, tantalum capacitor C_3 will explode, but the laser diode will not be damaged.

Depending on the type of laser diode, the value of series resistor R_1 must be adapted, although for most diodes, a value of 9–11 Ω is fine.

The circuit is built on a small piece of stripboard. If you have the skills and patience, you may well decide to etch a small printed-circuit board to which the components may be soldered at both sides.

The module can then be taken into use. Using a power supply of 3.5–6 V (at which power losses are smallest) and linking the modulation input to the +ve supply line, the diode should emit light.

A proper modulating voltage may be applied to the modulator input.

Figure 3-26
Circuit diagram of
basic automatic
power control (APC)

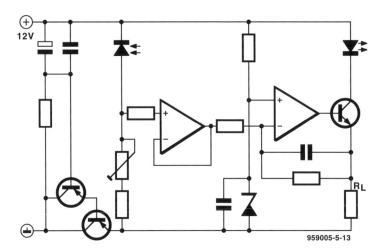

Thanks to the direct coupling, the potentiometer at the input provides the means for accurate power control. The modulation stage handles sinusoidal signals up to 2 MHz before the depth of modulation begins to diminish. It is noteworthy that a depth of modulation of 100% is achieved at frequencies of up to 2 MHz, which is not bad for a simple circuit.

Automatic Power Control (APC) drive
When an absolutely stable output power is required, an APC drive is indis-

pensable. The industry standard of this is shown in Figure 3-26. As mentioned earlier, this circuit stabilizes the optical output of the laser diode. With a supply voltage of 12 V, laboratory performance can be achieved. The circuit provides protection against voltage peaks and voltage variations. It can be used with most laser diodes, but make sure of the correct pinout.

Finally ...

... some general comments on how to deal with lasers safely.

- Make sure that the maximum ratings of current, voltage and temperature are not exceeded. The laser diode is particularly sensitive to voltage spikes that occur, for instance, when the power is switched on. Ample cooling with good heat removal are conducive to a long life. It is particularly important to stay well within the temperature limits when APC drive is used, since at high temperatures the optical output drops.
- Always discharge yourself of static electricity by touching a well-earthed object such as a water pipe before handling a laser diode. Static electricity can mean the end of the sensitive laser diode. Always use a well-earthed soldering iron.
- The laser diode is housed in an hermetically sealed case. Too much (pulling) force on the terminal pins may break the relevant internal connection, which means the destruction of the diode. In this context, also make sure that the temperature of the soldering iron does not exceed 260 °C and keep the soldering times to well within five seconds.
- Never touch the glass optical window of the diode with your fingers. Dirt and scratches on this window lessen the optical output power, and may mean that the beam can no longer be focused accurately. When the surface has become slightly dirty, clean it with a cotton bud and pure alcohol.

The active area of most diodes, where the laser beam emerges from the p-n junction, is rectangular, so that the emerging beam does not have a circular diameter, but may look like a bar. At a short distance from the diode this may be corrected to some extent with a lens, but a nicely round Gaussion beam is highly unlikely.

So-called TEM_{00} diodes, the diameter of whose light beam is exactly the same as that of a gas laser, have been available for some time. This has made the hope and wish of many constructors to be able to build a small and yet high-quality laser come a step closer. Green and blue laser diodes also exist, but they are not (yet) affordable for the average amateur. There are signs, however, that this may change within the very near future since several manufacturers have begun large-quantity production of these devices.

3.10 Multiline laser systems

Argon and He-Ne lasers generate a large number of different laser lines, that is, colours (or frequencies). The blue to green lines of the argon laser and the red one of an He-Ne laser are just the colours with which an attractive laser show can be set up. If you already own these types of laser, you belong to that select group of fortunate people who can construct a white light system with little effort and at relatively low cost. Well, we all know that 'white light' is a bit of an exaggeration, but nevertheless the mixing of the light of these two types of laser presents a worthwhile addition to the equipment for a successful show.

With a mixture of 35% blue, 35% green, and 30% red light, in conjunction with equal divergence and beam diameter, the resultant colour should not be far removed from white. Since this is seldom the case, unfortunately, it is hard to say what the result in your particular case will be. Dichroic colour filters can, however, remove most standard colours: green, blue, red, cyan and magenta. Difficulties arise with yellow, but even a 'yellowish' hue is a valuable addition to the range. This range refers, strictly speaking, only to the simple yet effective colour separation obtained with the aid of dichroic colour filters. If, in addition, intensity modulation (= z-modulation) is used, the range is extended to comprise a vast number of colours. This mixing unit, which is fairly complicated, is discussed in the next section.

Let us first consider how the two laser beams are merged. At first sight, this may look complicated, but in fact it is quite simple. It is only the mechanical construction which, in view of long-term stability, must be carried out with the utmost care. To build the mixing unit, you need the following materials and components:

• all-line argon laser with a power output of 80–150 mW, for instance, an ALC60x);
• He-Ne laser with a power output of 30–40 mW, for instance, an HNC

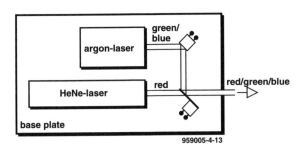

959005-4-13

Figure 3-27
Arrangement of
the lasers on the
aluminium sheet

Type 3000/4000);
- 10 mm thick sheet of aluminium the width and length of which depend on the dimensions of the lasers;
- two mirror holder with fine control, for instance, Type OSH2;
- a plane mirror 20 × 20 mm;
- a dichroic colour filter, cyan-reflecting, complementary: red.

These components are all fitted on the sheet of aluminium arranged as shown in Figure 3-27. A tip to simplify the tuning: fit the lasers in such a manner that their beams emerge at about the same position. You will see later how much time this will save you when you are setting up the two beams.

One of the mirror holders with fine control and fitted with the plane mirror, is placed in front of the argon laser.

The dichroic filter is glued to the other mirror holder and fitted in front of the He-Ne laser. If all items are placed in the correct positions, the light from the He-Ne laser passes through the filter, while the green/blue beam from the argon laser falls on to the filter sideways and is deflected by 90°, that is, in parallel with the He-Ne beam. It is fairly simple to direct the two beams on to the filter in such a way that they are co-incident. The beams are directed with the aid of the fine control of the holder with the filter so that they remain parallel even over long distances.

Colour separation
Now that we have combined the two beams with some difficulty, it is time to start separating them. But, to obtain pure colours, they have to be separated in a different manner from that in which they were combined. There are various methods of separating colours by means of software. Normally,

several colour filters are placed in the path of the beam to filter out various tints. Again, depending on the physical dimensions of the dichroic filters, there different ways of doing so. In the simplest and least expensive of these, use is made of actuators, such as those from the STP8 series. The dichroic filters are glued to the ends of the arms and placed in the path of the beam. With the use of an STP8 a switching frequency of almost 20 Hz is possible. But how can we construct a mixing unit with which a vast number of different colours can be reproduced?

Mixing unit

Even today, many show organizers use a colour mixing unit that in some mechanical way combines the three basic colours into a kaleidoscope. A basically analogue intensity control switches between the colours and controls the brightness. Such a mechanism may be constructed in a number of ways.

Figure 3-28
Arrangement for
standard RGB
blending

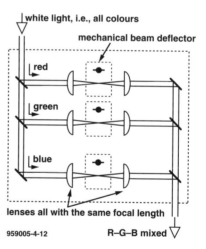

white light, i.e., all colours
mechanical beam deflector
red
green
blue
lenses all with the same focal length
959005-4-12   R–G–B mixed

Standard RGB. In this, the white laser beam is split into the three basic colours: red, blue and green—see Figure 3-28. The yellow line is not wanted. This is why resonator mirrors, intended to suppress the yellow line in a mixed-gas laser, are available specially optimized for this application. Each discrete basic colour is passed through an intensity control.

When two lenses with the same focal length, say, 50 mm, are used, the laser beam is focused to its minimum diameter (focus blanking works in the same way). Where the diameter of the beam is a minimum, the intensity of the beam is adjusted with a beam deflector. When all three basic colours (i.e., beams) are deflected completely, there is total blanking. This manner of mixing colours is fairly well established: these mixing units have been on the market since the laten1980s. However, in the mean time, better methods have been developed.

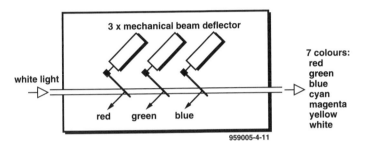

Figure 3-29
Colorbox

The Colorbox

If instead of a simple laser actuator a true beam deflector providing a large angle of deflection and equipped with dichroic filters is used, a fast, effective and high-quality mixing unit is obtained. Such units are commercially available under the name 'Colorbox' (see Figure 3-29). For satisfactory results, it is, of course, imperative to use first-class components. Three dichroic filters enable seven colours to be synthesized: the basic colours

red   a compound of magenta and yellow
green   a compound of cyan and yellow
blue   a compound of magenta and cyan

and the complementary colours

yellow
magenta
cyan

In the absence of any dichroism in the beam, the colour 'white' is also produced, or in any case light that looks 'whitish'. When all three filters are parallel to the beam, in theory there should be no light transmission. In practice that is not so, however, and this is because no filter is perfect: it always transmits some light that really should have been reflected.

Construction
A truly professional equipment is described that has proved its worth in many installations. The circuit is of industrial quality and has been developed especially for use with the Colorbox.

There are undoubtedly faster driver circuits, but these normally have the drawback that when the dichroic filters in the Colorbox are not balanced, or not well balanced, the spindle bearings of the beam deflectors may be overloaded or even become detached. And, of course, this always happens during a show or demonstration. The present, rather slower, circuit drives the beam deflectors in a way which ensures that even with exceptionally intensive use there is no risk of failure. Note, however, that good cooling of the output stage is important: the use of a small extractor fan is strongly advised. The very first prototype has been in service for over four years and has not failed once. This Colorbox is still in use today. Only the filters need to be replaced from time to time because they burn or become sticky. An important plus point of the system is that the colour separation is entirely loss-free, provided, of course, that there is no filter in the beam.

Building the fairly complex circuit requires the utmost accuracy and care. Any high-frequency oscillations may destroy the beam deflectors, because their magnets are demagnetized by the consequent high temperatures. In view of the cost of the deflectors, this is something that must be avoided. Accordingly, the design of the circuit ensures that the bandwidth is limited. Although steep edges are slightly rounded, the deflectors are accelerated.

In the author's experience, the mechanical beam deflectors Type G124 produced by General Scanning give the best results. Specialist mail order firms often have these deflectors available at prices lower than the manufacturer's price. The advantage of the G124 deflector is that its inductance is split into two: the two parts may be connected in series or in parallel. The series-connected inductor has a true (ohmic) resistance of about 7 Ω; in parallel-connected form, the d.c. resistance is around 2 Ω. When the inductor is connected in series, it becomes possible to use a higher voltage, and therefore a lower current, which means that the output stages do not get so hot.

Various other types of mechanical deflector may be used, but these invariably provide a smaller angle of deflection and normally have just one inductor. They are, however, rather less expensive.

The present circuit may be used with many types of mechanical beam deflector, although the component values are computed for use with the G124 model. The inputs are TTL-compatible and can, therefore, be driven by almost any computer. The asymmetric input signal is converted by an op amp into a symmetric (referred to earth) control voltage. This enables the deflectors to move in either direction (positive or negative) from their central position. In the case of the G124, the mechanical deflection amounts to 24°. Combining the deflector with a dichroic filter of 4×13 mm enables laser beams with a diameter of up 3 mm to be switched. The use of 45° filters is recommended, but standard 22° models also give satisfactory results.

Since January 1996, the CE-norm is mandatory also for electronic equipment in private use and it is, therefore, wise to bear the associated regulations in mind right from the start of construction.

Building the circuit, which is designed as an audio output stage with current feedback, requires a fair amount of experience in electronic construction. The design ensures a good slew rate and prevents overloading of the deflector spindles. The circuit may be built on a piece of

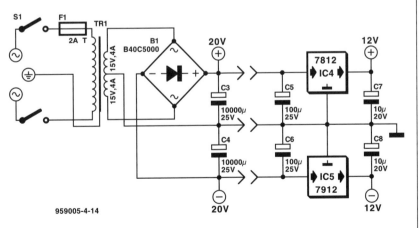

Figure 3-30
Power supply for the multiline laser

959005-4-14

Figure 3-31
Input stages of the
multiline laser

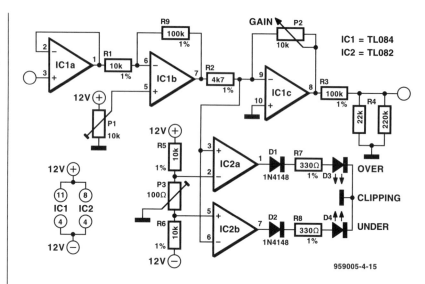

Figure 3-31
Input stages of the
multiline laser

959005-4-15

stripboard, but, as mentioned earlier, the greatest care must be observed. This is particularly important in the case of the earth connections.

Note that the output transistors have a high dissipation and must, therefore, be well cooled to give a good performance. Adequate cooling is provided by heat sinks with a surface area of 60–70 cm^2 When the unit is finished, it is best housed in a 2-unit high 19-in rack: this gives sufficient space for the toroidal transformers and large electrolytic capacitors.

For convenience's sake, the circuit has been split into three parts: the power supply (Figure 3-30), the input stages (Figure 3-31) and the output stages (Figure 3-32).

Power supply

The power supply provides two symmetrical outputs: a non-regulated one of ±20 V and a regulated one of ±12 V. The ±12 V is for powering the op amps and the ±20 V for the output transistors. The design of the power supply allows sufficient reserve power for its use with most types of open-loop deflectors.

Input stages

The input stages consist of voltage follower IC_{1a}, converter IC_{1b} (which renders the assymetric TTL input signals into symmetric control signals) and gain controller IC_{1c}. The clipping indication, based on IC_2, is not strictly necessary, but is very useful.

With the use of gain control P_2, the beam deflectors are driven to an extent where clipping just does not occur: this prevents their being overloaded at a later stage. Occasional spikes, however, remain noticeable.

Op amp IC_1 may be a quadruple type TL084; the rather slower Type LM324 is not quite suitable because it has a rather large offset.

Clipping indicator IC_2 is a dual op amp Type TL082.

Output stages

A dual op amp Type TL082 (IC_3) is used to provide a voltage follower, IC_{3a}, and a feedback amplifier IC_{3b}. Network R_{13}-C_1 between the op amp and the output transistors reduces the risk of high-frequency oscillations which, as mentioned earlier, may destroy the deflectors. It may be omitted, but this is best ascertained after satisfactory operation of the circuit has been proved. Omission of the network slightly im-

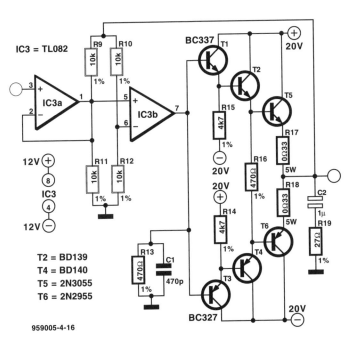

Figure 3-32
Output stages of the multiline laser.

959005-4-16

proves the slew rate.

Depending on the value of the d.c. resistance of the deflector coils, varying the value of emitter resistors R_{17} and R_{18} between 0.33 Ω and 1 Ω may improve the linearity of the output characteristic. In the prototype, this variation had little or no effect, however. When Type G124 deflectors are used, the value should be 1 Ω.

The circuit has been used on numerous occasions over the past four years and has proved to be totally reliable: it has not failed once in any respect. Bear in mind, however, that, as already mentioned, good cooling of the output transistors is imperative.

When professional software, such as, for instance, SCANplus Evolution, is used, the input stages may be driven directly by TTL signals. The author has measured switching frequencies greater than 100 Hz.

Components list for Figures 3-30, 3-31 and 3-32

Resistors:
R_1, R_5, R_6 = 10 kΩ*
R_2 = 4.7 kΩ*
R_3, R_9 = 100 kΩ*
R_4 = 20 kΩ* (22 kΩ* in parallel with 220 kΩ*)
R_7, R_8 = 330 Ω*
R_9–R_{12} = 10 kΩ*
R_{13}, R_{16} = 470 Ω*
R_{14}, R_{15} = 4.7 kΩ*
R_{17}, R_{18} = 0.33–1.0 Ω, 5 W, 5%, cermet (see text)
P_1, P_2 = 10 kΩ preset potentiometer
P_3 = 100 Ω preset potentiometer
* 1% metal film

Capacitors:
C_1 = 470 pF, ceramic
C_2 = 1 μF, electrolytic, bipolar
C_3, C_4 = 10 000 μF, 25 V, electrolytic
C_5, C_6 = 100 μF, 25 V, electrolytic
C_7, C_8 = 10 μF, 20 V

Semiconductors:
D_1, D_2 = 1N4148
D_3, D_4 = LED, 20 mA

*Components list for
Figures 3-30, 3-31
and 3-32 (cont'd)*

T_1 = BC337
T_2 = BD139
T_3 = BC327
T_4 = BD140
T_5 = 2N3055
T_6 = 2N2955

Integrated circuits:
IC_1 = TL084
IC_2, IC_3 = TL082
IC_4 = 7812
IC_5 = 7912

Miscellaneous:
B_1 = bridge rectifier B40C5000
Tr_1 = mains transformer, 2×15 V, 4 A
F_1 = fuse, 2 A, slow

3.11 Scanning system

Support for the QBASIC software used in this system is obtainable via mailbox 0049 7471 91665. The mailbox is operated via pull down menus. The protocol is 14400 baud, 8N1.

The circuit

The circuit of the digital-to-analogue converter (DAC) is identical to that of the DAI8 (an 8-bit industrial digital-to-analogue interface). The DAC can be connected directly to the printer port of a computer. Registers IC_1 and IC_2 function as a latch for the incoming information until all data for both spindles has been received. When that has happened, the data for both the X-axis and the Y-axis is passed to digital-to-analogue converters IC_3 and IC_4. The circuit diagram is shown in Figure 3-33. The power requirement is a single +5 V line, stabilized by a standard 3-pin regulator.

   The circuit diagram of the driver is shown in Figure 3-34. Each mechanical beam deflector or stepper motor needs a driver. Circuits IC_1 and IC_2 provide ample power for driving small scanners. It is particularly interesting that instead of mechanical beam deflectors stepper motors can be used. Depending on the size of step, the optical deflection may be as large as 30°. This means that a very useful, accurate and sturdy scanner may be constructed.

If stepper motors are used, one of the windings thereof, the hold coil, must be permanently linked to the +5 V line so as to produce a magnetic centre. The magnetic field of the second winding is combined

*Figure 3-33
Digital-to-
analogue con-
verter for the
scanning system*

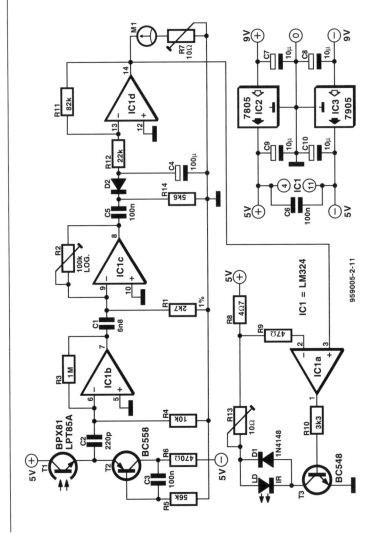

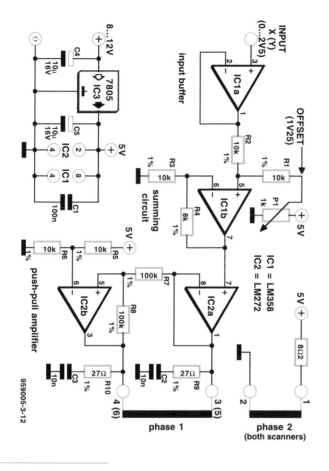

*Figure 3-34
Driver stages for
the scanning
system*

*Components list for
Figure 3-33*

R_1, R_2 = 390 Ω, 1%, metal film

C_1, C_2 = 1 μF, electrolytic, bipolar
C_3 = 0.001 μF

IC_1, IC_2 = 74HCT574
IC_3, IC_4 = ZN426
IC_5 = 7805

Components list for
Figure 3-34

R_1–R_3, R_5, R_6 = 10 kΩ*
R_4 = 8 kΩ*
R_7, R_8 = 100 kΩ*
R_9, R_{10} = 27 Ω*
* 1% metal film

C_1 = 0.001 μF, metallized polyester (MKT)
C_2, C_3 = 0.01 μF, metallized polyester (MKT)
C_4, C_5 = 10 μF, 16 V, electrolytic

IC_1 = LM358
IC_2 = LM272
IC_3 = 7805

with that of the first to enable the spindle to be moved in either direction from the magnetic centre. If a small stepper motor is used in conjunction with a small flat mirror, it will be seen that good speeds can be attained.

The circuit is conveniently built on a piece of stripboard, but note that the DAI8 may be purchased ready-made. The input of the converter can be connected directly to the LPT1 printer port of a computer via a screened printer cable. Make sure, however, that the cable is not longer than 7–8 m.

The inductor marked 'Phase 2' in Figure 3-34 is of import only when a stepper motor is driven. The value of the series resistor may have to be adapted according to the impedance of the inductor. If during a long period of operation it does not get hotter than lukewarm, its value is right.

The smaller the current through the hold coil, the faster the stepper motor can move, but at the same time the likelihood of fractions of incident light being transmitted increases. The use of a 10 Ω power potentiometer instead of the resistor provides a coarse control for setting the reaction time and the speed.

Software
The software enables the drawing, storing, loading and reading of illustrations in a siomple manner. The speed can be adapted by software to

the computer used. Where deemed necessary, the listing is provided with commentary and explanation. Output is via the printer port. The QBASIC interpreter is much more tolerant with reference to the interface components found in a number of computers than its predecessor GWBASIC. Nevertheless, some rare computers may have difficulties in getting the software to run properly, which are not resolved until the interface card has been replaced by another.

Where a QuickBasic compiler is available, the program may be converted to a faster *.EXE file. Since the program then also runs faster, it is necessary to lower the speed at which the data is sent. Operation is still untroubled when a 486 machine is used, but in case of a pentium-based computer the deflectors can no longer match the operating speed.

As mentioned at the beginning of this section, the SCANplus 3.0 software may be obtained as freeware from the mailbox. This enables the processing and executing of a laser animation in a convenient manner. This program is rather more complex and generates control signals for two spindles – ideal for this application.

Beware, however, since the simpler program has consequences for the operating speed. The software was written originally for a 286 run ning at 12 MHz, which is fairly slow compared with current computers. When a 386 machine is used, the control signals will be sent at an appreciable speed, while in case of a 486 computer the deflectors will transmit fractions of light when they should not. If this happens, the variable CPU Slow-down in the CFG file must be modified or the computer slowed down by switching off the shadow RAM or cache memory.

3 Applications

```
'_____
'ProgName:SCANUL.BAS              written by: A.Heilig
'Ordered by :es-Lasersysteme          Date: 21.03.94
'_____

'Function :Draw figures for a laser show using the arrow keys
'          :Resolution 640x480 (VGA)
'          :Save figures on disk
'          :Compute reference points and store in array
'          :Compute circles
'          :Export values in array to LPT
'          :File selection using arrow keys
'_____

DECLARE SUB StartVereinbarungen ()
DECLARE SUB GetFN (Ext$, FilN$)
DECLARE SUB Dateiuebersicht ()
DECLARE SUB Koordinatentest ()
DECLARE SUB AusgabeZeichnen ()
DECLARE SUB TCodeauswerten ()
DECLARE SUB SaeubereZFeld ()
DECLARE SUB Cursor (Farbe!)
DECLARE SUB WertevonDisk ()
DECLARE SUB Oberflaeche ()
DECLARE SUB AusgabeDAI8 ()
DECLARE SUB FehlerKreis ()
DECLARE SUB FTastenStop ()
DECLARE SUB FTastenEin ()
DECLARE SUB Speichern ()
DECLARE SUB Zeichnen ()
DECLARE SUB FTasten ()
DECLARE SUB Ausgabe ()
DECLARE SUB Kreis ()


REM $DYNAMIC            'Arrays are dynamic (erasable) for EXE!
DIM SHARED Enter        AS INTEGER   'Declare variable
                                     '"Enter" as an integer,
                                     'available to all
```

```
                                    'procedures
DIM SHARED Taste          AS STRING
DIM SHARED links          AS INTEGER
DIM SHARED rechts         AS INTEGER
DIM SHARED hoch           AS INTEGER
DIM SHARED runter         AS INTEGER
DIM SHARED X              AS INTEGER
DIM SHARED Y              AS INTEGER
DIM SHARED Punkt          AS INTEGER
DIM SHARED LP             AS INTEGER
DIM SHARED LPunkt         AS INTEGER
DIM SHARED sxf            AS INTEGER

DIM SHARED X(1 TO 10000)    AS INTEGER  'arrays for 'radius
                                                coordinates
DIM SHARED Y(1 TO 10000)        AS INTEGER
DIM SHARED xAusgabe(1 TO 10000)  AS INTEGER   'arrays for export
DIM SHARED yAusgabe(1 TO 10000)  AS INTEGER
VIEW PRINT 1 TO 25
X = 128
Y = 128
CALL Oberflaeche

CALL FTasten

DO
  CALL TCodeauswerten            'fetch key action
  IF Enter = 1 AND Punkt > 0 THEN
    Punkt = Punkt + 1
    FOR APunkt = 1 TO Punkt
     X(Punkt) = X - 1
     Y(Punkt) = Y - 1
     IF APunkt = Punkt THEN EXIT FOR
     LINE (X(APunkt), Y(APunkt))-(X(APunkt + 1),Y(APunkt + 1)), 15
    NEXT APunkt
    LOCATE 14, 68: PRINT Punkt
```

```
   END IF

  IF Enter = 1 AND Punkt = 0 THEN
    Punkt = Punkt + 1
    X(Punkt) = X - 1
    Y(Punkt) = Y - 1
    FOR APunkt = 1 TO Punkt
     LINE (X(APunkt), Y(APunkt))-(X(APunkt), Y(APunkt)), 15
    NEXT APunkt
    LOCATE 14, 68: PRINT Punkt
  END IF


  CALL TCodeauswerten

LOOP

END

Speichern:      'mark "Speichern" as jump address
                             'for F2 key
    CALL FTastenStop
    CALL Speichern      'call procedure "Speichern"
    CALL FTastenEin
    RETURN                  'continue program where
                             'F2 key was pressed
Ende:
    CALL FTastenStop
    KEY OFF
    DEF SEG            'restore segment address to
                    'original value (important!!!)
    CLS
    END

Clearscreen:
    CALL FTastenStop
    CALL SaeubereZFeld
```

```
        CALL FTastenEin
        RETURN

Ausgabe:
        CALL FTastenStop
        CALL Ausgabe
        CALL FTastenEin
        RETURN

Dateiuebersicht:
        CALL FTastenStop
        CALL Dateiuebersicht
        CALL FTastenEin
        RETURN

Kreis:
        CALL FTastenStop
        CALL Kreis
        CALL FTastenEin
        RETURN

REM $STATIC
SUB Ausgabe
'
'Compute dots between corners points
'_____--
CALL WertevonDisk
CALL SaeubereZFeld
VIEW PRINT 18 TO 28
CLS 2
VIEW PRINT
LOCATE 25, 1: INPUT "No. of points between ref. points: ", Schritte
LOCATE 25, 1: PRINT SPC(40);
IF Schritte = 0 THEN Schritte = 1
FOR Ag = 1 TO LP - 1
    sx = X(Ag)                  'fetch x-axis start values from the array
```

```
sy = Y(Ag)
IF Ag = LP THEN Ag = Ag - 1
zx = X(Ag + 1)              'fetch x-axis target values from the array
zy = Y(Ag + 1)
rvx = zx - sx              'direction vector x-axis
rvy = zy - sy              'direction vector y-axis
dx = sx - zx              'difference x
dy = sy - zy              'difference y
vl = INT(SQR(dy ^ 2 + dx ^ 2))         'length of vector
PSET (sx + 1, sy + 1), 14             'draw first point
sxf = sxf + 1
xAusgabe(sxf) = X(Ag)
yAusgabe(sxf) = 255 - Y(Ag)
FOR apt = 1 TO vl STEP Schritte
  ap = apt / vl            'factor for extra points
  apx = sx + (ap * rvx)
  apy = sy + (ap * rvy)
  sxf = sxf + 1
  xAusgabe(sxf) = apx
  yAusgabe(sxf) = 255 - apy
  PSET (apx + 1, apy + 1), 14             'draw reference points
NEXT apt
sxf = sxf + 1
xAusgabe(sxf) = zx
yAusgabe(sxf) = 255 - zy
PSET (zx + 1, zy + 1), 14             'draw last point
IF Ag = LP THEN EXIT FOR
NEXT Ag
CALL AusgabeDAI8

END SUB


SUB AusgabeDAI8
'
'transmit contents of arrays to printer port LPT
'_____
```

```
lpt = &H378
lptsr = &H37A
LOCATE 25, 1: PRINT "Sending data ... stop with Esc!"
DO
     FOR LPunkt = 1 TO sxf
      OUT lpt, xAusgabe(LPunkt)
      OUT lptsr, 2: OUT lptsr, 0
      OUT lpt, yAusgabe(LPunkt)
      OUT lptsr, 4: OUT lptsr, 0
     'if necessary insert a delay loop here
     NEXT LPunkt
LOOP WHILE INKEY$ <> CHR$(27)
LOCATE 25, 1: PRINT SPC(60);
sxf = 0
LP = 0

END SUB
SUB Cursor (Farbe)
'
'draw with the cursor (change colour for reading or erasing)
'_____

IF Farbe = 15 THEN Farbe = 14
PRESET (X, Y), Farbe

END SUB

SUB Dateiuebersicht
'
'show all files with the extension .esp
'_____

VIEW PRINT 18 TO 28
CLS 2
LOCATE 18, 1: FILES "*.esp"
COLOR 12: LOCATE 28, 10: PRINT "<< press any key >>"
SLEEP
COLOR 7
```

```
CLS 2
VIEW PRINT


END SUB


SUB FehlerKreis
'
'show errors (if any) in the circle drawing process
'_____
VIEW PRINT 18 TO 28
CLS 2
LOCATE 20, 2: PRINT "Incorrect circle data entered."
LOCATE 21, 2: PRINT "Erase field with F4 and use arrow keys and "
LOCATE 22, 2: PRINT "Enter to indicate the centre and then the "
LOCATE 23, 2: PRINT "radius by moving the cursor the right "
LOCATE 24, 2: PRINT "and confirm the position by pressing the "
LOCATE 25, 2: PRINT "Enter key; next, press F7 to"
LOCATE 26, 2: PRINT "compute the circle."
VIEW PRINT


END SUB
SUB FTasten
'
'activation of function keys en keyname/jump address allocation
'_____
KEY ON        'show keynames defined by the user
ON KEY(2) GOSUB Speichern
ON KEY(3) GOSUB Ende
ON KEY(4) GOSUB Clearscreen
ON KEY(5) GOSUB Ausgabe
ON KEY(6) GOSUB Dateiuebersicht
ON KEY(7) GOSUB Kreis

KEY(2) ON: KEY 2, " Save    "
KEY(3) ON: KEY 3, " End    "
KEY(4) ON: KEY 4, " New    "
```

```
KEY(5)  ON: KEY 5, " Do    "
KEY(6)  ON: KEY 6, " Dir     "
KEY(7)  ON: KEY 7, " Circle "
KEY(8)  ON: KEY 8, "          "
KEY(9)  ON: KEY 9, "          "
KEY(10) ON: KEY 10, "         "

END SUB

SUB FTastenEin
'
'activate function keys
'_____
KEY(1)  ON
KEY(2)  ON
KEY(3)  ON
KEY(4)  ON
KEY(5)  ON
KEY(6)  ON
KEY(7)  ON
KEY(8)  ON
KEY(9)  ON
KEY(10) ON

END SUB

SUB FTastenStop
'
'disable function keys
'_____
KEY(1)  STOP
KEY(2)  STOP
KEY(3)  STOP
KEY(4)  STOP
KEY(5)  STOP
KEY(6)  STOP
```

```
KEY(7)  STOP
KEY(8)  STOP
KEY(9)  STOP
KEY(10) STOP


END SUB

SUB GetFN (Ext$, FilN$)
'
'get filename
'_____
LOCATE 18, 1
FILES Ext$                                'show files X% = 1: Y% = 19
DO
    FilN$ = ""                            'get file names from screen
    FOR i% = 0 TO 11                  'all characters
     FilN$ = FilN$ + CHR$(SCREEN(Y%, X% + i%))
    NEXT i%
    FilN$ = RTRIM$(FilN$)
    LOCATE Y%, X%
    PRINT "█"; FilN$; "█"   'show names in inverse video
    DO
     Key$ = INKEY$
    LOOP UNTIL LEN(Key$)                  'wait for key action
    LOCATE Y%, X%
    PRINT FilN$; SPC(3);            'show names in normal video
    SELECT CASE ASC(RIGHT$(Key$, 1))'which key
     CASE 13, 27
       EXIT DO                      '<<Return>>or <<Escape>>: end
     CASE 72
       Y% = Y% + (Y% >> 19)         'cursor up
     CASE 80                                'cursor down
       IF CHR$(SCREEN(Y% + 1, X%)) <> " " THEN Y% = Y% + 1
     CASE 75
       X% = X% + 18 * (X% > 1) 'cursor left
     CASE 77
```

```
       X% = X% - 18 * (X% < 54)'cursor right
     CASE ELSE
    END SELECT
LOOP

END SU

e
SUB Koordinatentest
'
'limit pen coordinates to 8 bits
'-----------------------------
IF X < 1 THEN X = 1
IF Y < 1 THEN Y = 1
IF X > 256 THEN X = 256
IF Y > 256 THEN Y = 256


END SUB

SUB Kreis
'
'centre of circle (point 1) and radius (point 2)
'-----------------------------------------
SELECT CASE Punkt
   CASE IS > 2
    CALL FehlerKreis
    EXIT SUB
   CASE IS = 0
    CALL FehlerKreis
    EXIT SUB
   END SELECT

VIEW PRINT 18 TO 28
```

```
CLS 2
VIEW PRINT

LOCATE 15, 70: PRINT "Circle"

KreismitteX = X(1)                              'centre
X1 = X(1)                                       '
KreismitteY = Y(1)                              'centre
LINE (X(1), Y(1))-(X(2), Y(2)), 0
Radius = ABS(X(2) - X(1))
PI = 3.14159
PI2 = PI * 2                        'circle = 2 pi
Skala = 20 / PI2                'no. of points on circle
Punkt = 0
DO
  IF Punkt = 21 THEN EXIT DO
  Punkt = Punkt + 1
  X(Punkt) = INT((SIN(Punkt / Skala) * Radius) + X1)
  Y(Punkt) = INT(KreismitteY - (COS(Punkt / Skala) * Radius))
  IF Y(Punkt) > 255 THEN Y(Punkt) = 255
  IF X(Punkt) > 255 THEN X(Punkt) = 255
  IF Y(Punkt) < 0 THEN Y(Punkt) = 0
  IF X(Punkt) < 0 THEN X(Punkt) = 0
  PSET (X(Punkt), Y(Punkt))
LOOP
LOCATE 15, 70: PRINT SPC(5);

END SUB

SUB Oberflaeche
'
   CASE IS = 0
    CALL FehlerKreis
    EXIT SUB
'set up opening screen of program for drawing and value entry
```

```
'----------------------------------------------------------------
SCREEN 12
CLS
COLOR 14
LOCATE 5, 50: PRINT "SCAN Ultra-lite 1.1"
COLOR 7
LINE (0, 0)-(257, 257), 7, B
LOCATE 11, 48: PRINT "drawing pen coordinates"
LOCATE 12, 60: PRINT "x-as:"; SPC(5); "pixel"
LOCATE 13, 60: PRINT "y-as:"; SPC(5); "pixel"
LOCATE 14, 60: PRINT "points:"
END SUB

SUB SaeubereZFeld
'
're-initialise drawing array
'-------------------------
VIEW (1, 1)-(256, 256)
CLS 1
VIEW
Punkt = 0
X = 128
Y = 128

END SUB

SUB Speichern
'
'procedure for storage of calculated x and y-axis values
'in a sequential file
'----------------------------------------------------------------
LOCATE 25, 1: INPUT "Name of file to be saved: ", Dateiname$
LOCATE 25, 1: PRINT SPC(40);

OPEN Dateiname$ + ".esp" FOR OUTPUT AS #1 'open figure file for
```

```
'writing
FOR SPunkt = 1 TO Punkt               'save all points
    PRINT #1, X(SPunkt), Y(SPunkt)    'write values to disk
NEXT SPunkt
CLOSE #1                           'close figures file
END SUB


SUB TCodeauswerten
'
'recognise RIGHT, LEFT, UP, DOWN, ESC and Enter
'-----------------------------------------------
DEF SEG = &H40            'segment address at 40 hex
WHILE Taste = ""             'wait for key
    Taste = INKEY$
WEND

 Enter = 0
  hoch = 0
  runter = 0
  rechts = 0
  links = 0

IF ASC(RIGHT$(Taste, 1)) = 13 THEN
    Enter = 1
END IF

IF ASC(RIGHT$(Taste, 1)) = 77 THEN
    rechts = 1
    CALL Cursor(0)
    TStatus% = PEEK(&H17)
    IF TStatus% > 159 THEN TStatus% = TStatus% - 128
    IF TStatus% > 32 THEN X = X + 5
    X = X + 1
    CALL Koordinatentest
    CALL Cursor(15)
```

```
END IF

IF ASC(RIGHT$(Taste, 1)) = 75 THEN
    links = 1
    CALL Cursor(0)
    TStatus% = PEEK(&H17)
    IF TStatus% > 159 THEN TStatus% = TStatus% - 128
    IF TStatus% > 32 THEN X = X - 5
    X = X - 1
    CALL Koordinatentest
    CALL Cursor(15)
END IF

IF ASC(RIGHT$(Taste, 1)) = 72 THEN
    hoch = 1
    CALL Cursor(0)
    TStatus% = PEEK(&H17)
    IF TStatus% > 159 THEN TStatus% = TStatus% - 128
    IF TStatus% > 32 THEN Y = Y - 5
    Y = Y - 1
    CALL Koordinatentest
    CALL Cursor(15)
END IF

IF ASC(RIGHT$(Taste, 1)) = 80 THEN
    runter = 1
    CALL Cursor(0)
    TStatus% = PEEK(&H17)
    IF TStatus% > 159 THEN TStatus% = TStatus% - 128
    IF TStatus% > 32 THEN Y = Y + 5
    Y = Y + 1
    CALL Koordinatentest

    CALL Cursor(15)
END IF
```

```
Taste = INKEY$                      'key released?


LOCATE 12, 68: PRINT X - 1      'export pen coordinates
LOCATE 13, 68: PRINT Y - 1


DEF SEG = 0                     'restore segment address to
                          'original value


END SUB


SUB WertevonDisk
'
'read saved x- and y-axis values
'from the sequential file "*.ESP"
'---------------------------------------
VIEW PRINT 18 TO 28
CLS 2
VIEW PRINT
GetFN "*.esp", File$
Dateiname$ = File$
IF Dateiname$ = "" THEN CALL WertevonDisk
OPEN Dateiname$ FOR INPUT AS #1            'open figures file
WHILE EOF(1) = 0                     'read to end of file
    LP = LP + 1                  'increment array pointer
    INPUT #1, X(LP), Y(LP)            'data from disk to array
WEND
CLOSE #1                   'close figures file


END SUB
```

3.12 Seismograph

The seismograph is a fairly difficult project, which requires good experience of electronics as well as of mechanical construction. Since the instrument upon completion is highly sensitive, all mechanical parts must fit correctly. In short, the utmost care and precision is required in completing the work.

First, a brief refresher in seismology. Earthquakes are motions of the earth crust caused, in most cases, by displacement of tectonic plates along a fault. Although the amount of displacement may be small, a matter of inches only, the destruction wrought at the surface may be very great.

Geologists have tried for ages, mostly unsuccessfully, to predict the occurrence of an earthquake. Nevertheless, slight earth movements occur that often indicate the likelihood of a more serious and dangerous earthquake. Such small earth movements, often unnoticed except by sensitive instruments, occur regularly in many parts of the world and most of them are not followed by a serious earthquake. It is only by continuous observations over long periods that an earthquake can be predicted with any accuracy.

Seismograph

A seismograph is a device that records seismic information. Its pickup is called a geophone, which may be compared with a dynamic microphone, since it transforms ground motion (rather than air motion) into a tiny electrical signal. Spurious measurements are precluded by locating the geophone, which is a massive, complex instrument, in an underground bunker. The tiny electrical signals are amplified and then passed via a cable, or wireless transmission, to the seismic station where they are processed and recorded. In days gone by the ground motion was registered with the aid of a galvanometer which had a pen on a long needle fitted to its pointer. Nowadays, of course, special measurement computers are used.

Richter scale

The intensity of seismic waves is measured on the basis of their amplitude according to the scale developed by Charles Francis Richter (1900–1985), an American physicist and geologist. The scale was first proposed in 1927. The amplitude depends on the depth of the epicentre (earthquake focus), the distance of the geophone from the epicentre, the travel path, and vari-

Intensity	Released energy (Joule)	Energy comparable to
−2	60	100 watt light bulb
−1	$2{\times}10^3$	lowest recordable vibration
0	$60{\times}10^3$	0.5 kg TNT exploding
1	$2{\times}10^6$	2 heavy lorries at 70 MPH
2	$60{\times}10^6$	recordable but not noticeable
3	$2{\times}10^9$	lowest noticeable vibration
4	$60{\times}10^9$	1000 ton TGNT exploding
5	$2{\times}10^{12}$	light destruction
6	$60{\times}10^{12}$	moderate destruction
7	$2{\times}10^{15}$	heavy destruction
8	$60{\times}10^{15}$	very serious destruction
9	$2{\times}10^{18}$	catastrophic destruction
10	$60{\times}10^{18}$	total ernergy used in USA in a year

ous other factors. The magnitude, M, of a shallow (that is, close to the surface) quake is computed by the equation

$$M = \log(A/T) + 1.66\log\Delta + 3.3,$$

where A is the maximum amplitude, T is the period, and Δ is the epicentral angular distance between the earthquake and the geophone. It is seen that the scale arranged on the basis of this equation is logarithmic, in other words, a quake with strength 6 is ten times as strong as one with strength 5. As a comparison, a quake of strength 5 is very noticeable, one of 6 can damage buildings, and one of 7 can cause very serious damage.

One of the most notorious areas for earthquakes is along the San Andreas fault in California; another one is in the Swabian Alps in Germany. Building construction and techniques in such areas, which make buildings more 'flexible', have greatly reduced the damage caused by medium quakes that have occurred over the past few decades.

Reliable relative measurements are only attainable when the measurement results are regularly processed and recorded over a period of time. Since the instrument is very sensitive, naturally occuring earth motions must be distinguished from vibrations caused by, say, heavy traffic. A computer

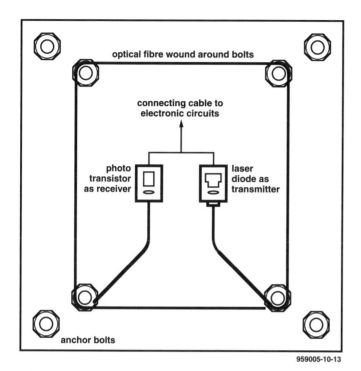

Figure 3-35
Basic set up of
seismograph

enables the seismic data to be registered at regular intervals. This makes it fairly straightforward to carry out measurements over a period of time.

Technology

In comparison with the usual mechanical seismograph. the present laser seismograph is an ultra-modern instrument with many advantages. It is no exaggeration to say that if it is constructed with the necessary care and precision, it is comparable as far as sensitivity is concerned to many professional instruments. The principle of operation is fairly straightforward (see Figure 3-35).

When a laser beam is passed through an optical fibre, any movement of the fibre causes interference patterns which can be used to cause a phototransistor to conduct to some degree. The variations in the intensity of the laser light can be converted to a proportional voltage by a suitable external circuit. A slight movement of the fibre causes little interference, whereas strong movements may result in total extinction. If the fibre is sus-

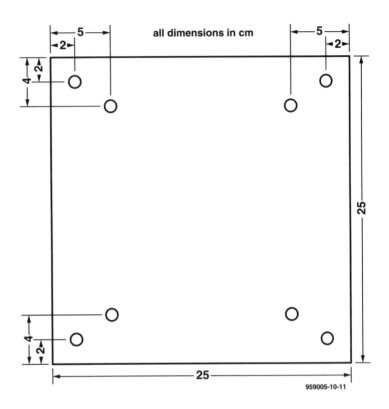

all dimensions in cm

959005-10-11

pended too loosely, even slight air movements (light breeze) cause the measurements to be unreliable. When the fibre is suspended too tightly, however, many vibrations may not be registered. This may be an advantage when the seismograph is located near a busy road. Experiments with the prototype showed that if the seismograph is constructed carefully it can react even to the human voice.

When laser light is propagated through air, there is one single coherent beam. When it is transmitted through an optical fibre, it undergoes multiple reflections – which is, after all, the basis of operation via an optical fibre. If, however, the optical paths differ, and the reflections are superimposed on to each other, extinction may occur. Some light waves arrive at the end of the fibre earlier than others owing to their optical paths being shorter resulting from a smaller number of times they are internally reflected. This process reduces the coherence which, in extreme circumstances, can be lost altogether. In that case, the laser light is not much better than the light from a torch. This phenomenon becomes clearer when a

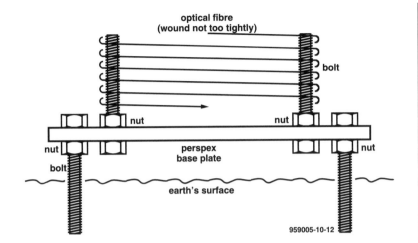

Figure 3-37
Construction of
the geophone
(detector)

laser beam is coupled to a thin optical fibre via a lens with a short focal length. If the effluent beam is directed unaided on to a white surface, a spot of light is seen whose diameter varies, depending on the focus of the input lens. This is, however, not of much interest for a seismograph, where the variation of illumination within the effluent cone is the important aspect. When the fibre is moved and the spot of light observed, it will be seen that the light-to-dark pattern within the spot varies. The dark areas are caused by extinction because of interference (superimposition of wave peaks on to troughs); whereas the brighter areas are the result of amplification (superimposition of wave peaks on to wave peaks or wave troughs on to wave troughs).

When this cone of light (spot of light) is focused on to the light sensitive area (the base) of the photo transistor, the basic receiver is ready. Care must be taken, however, to ensure that the laser power is not too great to prevent the photo transistor being driven into saturation. The output of the photo transistor is applied to the optical receiver described in Section 3.13. Bear in mind that when an He-Ne laser is used as a continuous-wave (cw) transmitter, a very small power output suffices: 0.5–1.0 mW is more than enough. For that reason, a low-power semiconductor (diode) laser is to be preferred. When the circuit is taken into use for the first time, connect its output to a small audio amplifier or, directly, to a pair of headphones. Even a slight vibration of the base plate causes a dull rumble. The input sensitivity must be adjusted according to circumstances.

Construction

Apart from correctly mounting the optical fibre cable, the construction is not all that difficult. If at all possible, use an optical glass fibre cable; a synthetic fibre may be used in an emergency, but only a glass fibre breaks cleanly so that its ends can be ground precisely and smoothly. A really smoothly polished end-surface is imperative for good coupling between it and the laser beam without any diffraction.

A length of fibre cable of about 4.5 m is needed. Remove about 15 mm of insulation at both ends. Using a new Stanley knife or similar (but sharp!), score the fibre about 10 mm from one end and break off the end. Inspect the surface of the fracture with a magnifying glass. The surface should be reasonably level and clear; if it is not, it must be polished. This polishing normally requires a fairly expensive set of tools, but in our case, it is done with wet-and-dry emery paper no. 600 (very fine). Use a block of wood as in Figure 3-13 (Section 3.7), insert the end of the fibre cable into it, wet the emery paper and start polishing. During this process, regularly inspect the surface with a magnifying glass. With careful work and a little luck, the fibre cable should soon be ready for installation.

Next, drill a small hole in the top of the photo transistor case, exactly at the centre above the light-sensitive area. Fasten the glass fibre cable at right angles in this hole with epoxy resin. If you use synthetic fibre cable, use a photo transistor already drilled in this manner. Such devices are available from some of the better mail order firms or retailers.

While the epoxy resin is setting, the base plate can be prepared, This consists of a 25 × 25 cm, 10 mm thick sheet of perspex which is available from most do-it-yourself shops and builders merchants. If you want a really sturdy assembly, use 25 mm thick perspex, which is available from specialist synthetic materials merchants.

Drill eight holes in the perspex as shown in Figure 3-36. A hand drill is best, but if you use an electric drill, set it to a low speed, since high speeds may cause the perspex to melt. Also, do not exert too much pressure on the perspex during the drilling, since this may cause hairline cracks.

Fix a 30 mm bolt and nut firmly in each of the four inner holes (see Figure 3-37). Wind the fibre cable clockwise around these bolts: not too tightly and not too loosely. Too tight a winding reduces the sensitivity and increases the risk of the cable breaking. If the winding is too loose, the turns may slip down or off the bolts. It may take a few times before you have the cable at exactly the right tension. Check the correct operation with the general-purpose optical receiver described in Section 3.13 and a pair of headphones. With a little luck and dexterity, it will all be ready in a matter of minutes.

The photo transistor and laser diode must be fixed firmly to the base plate: the best method depends strongly on the manner in which the modules are constructed. Gluing is the simplest, while fixing with a metal clip is the most elegant and practical.

If the seismograph is set up in the open air, a watertight enclosure is indispensable. The transmitter and receiver are connected via screened, rubber insulated cable to the nearby electronic circuits and computer, which are, of course, indoors.

To ensure good performance during very cold weather, the ICs should have a ceramic case instead of the usual plastic one. Ceramic models have a much wider operating temperature range than the plastic ones. Also, bear in mind that hard or hardened glue can break in low temperatures; it is therefore better to use a glue that remains soft, such as two component epoxy resin or a silicone-based one.

Fix bolts and nuts firmly in the outer holes in the base plate, but pointing the other way from those in the inner holes. With these, the base plate is secured firmly to, say, a heavy slab of concrete that is placed on or slightly in the soil. The heavier the concrete, the more spurious vibrations caused by, for instance, traffic will be suppressed.

After the geophone has been anchored to the soil, it is possible, if conditions so require, to slacken or increase the tension on the fibre cable. Finally, cover the assembly with a watertight hood. This completes the mechanical construction.

Usage

Connect the optical receiver temporarily to the incoming cable from the geophone. Use a pair of headphones to listen to the vibrations of the earth, which, because of the high sensitivity of the instrument, are clearly audible. If you live in the vicinity of a road carrying heavy traffic, you will also hear all the road vibrations. This background noise will make it difficult to hear the natural seismic vibrations and quakes. If, however, you live in a very quiet area, you may have to ask someone to perform a wardance around the geophone. If all is well, the receiver can be connected permanently to the incoming cable.

Digital computer interface

Headphones are useful for testing the system, but they do not enable real measurements to be carried out. For this, a computer is needed. To enable the measurement data to be processed and registered, they may be quantized at a resolution of 8 bits and then passed to the computer via its printer port. It is, however, much better to use a general-purpose parallel interface card which are described in all sorts and sizes in various books and magazines. The card used with the prototype is based on the well-known Type PIO8255 parallel interface IC, which has a total of 24 I/O lines available, of which only eight are needed.

The analogue output voltage of the optical receiver must be converted into a digital signal by an analogue-to-digital converter (ADC) such as the ZN427 before it can be transferred to the parallel port of the computer. A simple program then makes it possible for measurement data to be read and stored on a hard disk at regular intervals.

It is, however, clearly impossible to store all the vibrations recorded over the course of time: the hard disk would be full in no time. This means that the software must evaluate the dynamics of the incoming signals and only record them if they show variations above a certain level. When that is done, only some vibrations will be stored and we can be certain that moderate to severe seismic waves are registered for later analysis. This software filter must be set so that man-made vibrations, such as those of passing traffic, are suppressed. The computer will then register data whose signal level is clearly higher than the average background noise level.

The writing of such a program is outside the scope of this book, but there are plenty of books and magazines that give guidance on how to write a suitable program yourself.

Analogue-to-digital converters (ADCs) are described in detail from time to time in magazines like *Elektor Electronics*.

3.13 General-purpose optical receivers

Many projects in this chapter are based on the transfer of light or data. This clearly requires some sort of receiver, preferably one which because of its general design is suitable not only for these projects but also for those developed by readers. Several suitable receivers are described in this section, including some intended for switching purposes only. Their construction is straightforward and all have been tested thoroughly and used in practice over periods of time.

AM receiver

The circuit in Figure 3-38 shows an amplitude-modulation (AM) receiver that uses a photo-transistor, T_1, as detector. It is followed by an amplifier, IC_1, which is very stable and insensitive to interference. The sensitivity of

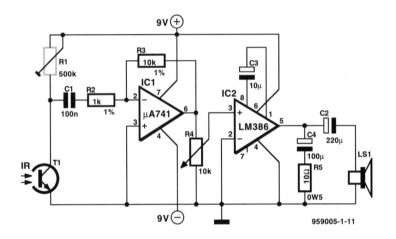

Figure 3-38
Circuit diagram of
general-purpose AM
receiver

R_1 = 500 kΩ multiturn preset potentiometer
R_2 = 1 kΩ, metal film, 1%
R_3 = 10 kΩ, metal film, 1%
R_4 = 10 kΩ potentiometer
R_5 = 10 Ω, 0.5 W

C_1 = 0.001 μF, ceramic disc
C_2 = 220 μF, electrolytic
C_3 = 10 μF, electrolytic
C_4 = 100 μF, electrolytic

T_1 = sensitive infra-red photo transistor

IC_1 = μA741
IC_2 = LM386

Components list for
Figure 3-38

---

the receiver proper is set with R_1.

A second amplifier, IC_2, drives a small loudspeaker, LS_1. The volume is controlled with R_4.

The overall receiver is decoupled by means of capacitors. If it is used in conjunction with the seismograph described in Section 3.12, it is better to omit capacitors C_1 and C_2 and replace them with a wire bridge. This results in a direct-coupled receiver.

The detector may be any type of infra-red photo transistor available.

The receiver is powered by a symmetric supply, which may be provided by two 9-V batteries.

For experimental purposes, the receiver may be housed in a small plastic case. It is not really necessary to design a printed-circuit board for it: it is easily built on a piece of stripboard. This also makes it easier to modify the circuit at a later date. Nevertheless, the construction should be carried out with care and neat soldering to prevent spurious oscillations occurring that may spoil or distort the measurements and would give rise to the wrong conclusions.

The phototransistor should be mounted in a small tube of appropriate inner diameter. This prevents not only interference by ambient light and other sources of light, but also gives the detector some directivity. Mind the polarity of the transistor when soldering it into place: the detector will still work with incorrect polarity, but its sensitivity is then much reduced.

Usage
Set sensitivity control R_1 to the centre of its travel, volume control R_4 to nminimum and connect the receiver to the two batteries or other ± 9-V power supply as the case may be. When the volume control is turned gently, a dull hum should become audible: this is the 50 Hz hum emitted by the mains supply via the room lights. When the lights are not on, this hum will not be heard, so do turn them on for this test. If you still do not hear anything, there is a fault somewhere. Check all connections, junctions, components, and so on. If all these are all right, the receiver must work satisfactorily.

PLL FM receiver
The receiver just described is excellent for a number of experiments in which amplitude modulation (AM) is used. The sound quality of wireless AM transfer is not very good, however, and not really suitable for serious

applications. The transfer by a carrier wave that is frequency-modulated (FM) by the audio signal gives a much better sound quality. A suitable receiver for such a wave is shown in Figure 3-39.

As in the AM receiver, the detector is an infra-red photo transistor, T_1, followed by amplifier IC_1. The output of the amplifier is applied to phase-locked loop (PLL) IC_2, which demodulates the incoming signal around a

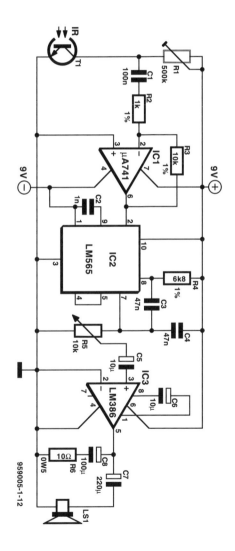

Figure 3-39
Circuit diagram of a
PLL FM receiver

R_1 = 22 kΩ*
R_2 = 1 kΩ*
R_3 = 10 kΩ*
R_4 = 6.8 kΩ*
R_5 = 10 kΩ*
R_6 = 10 Ω, 0.5 W
* = metal film, 1%

C_1 = 0.001 μF ceramic disk
C_2 = 0.1 μF metallized polyester (MKT)
C_3, C_4 = 0.047 μF metallized polyester (MKT)
C_5, C_6 = 10 μF, electrolytic
C_7 = 220 μF, electrolytic
C_8 = 100 μF, electrolytic

T_1 = infra-red photo transistor

IC_1 = μA741
IC_2 = NE565

central frequency of 39.75 kHz, and applies the resulting audio signals to audio amplifier IC_3. The central PLL frequency, f_c, of 39.75 kHz results from the design values specified in Figure 3-39. Replacing R_4 by a multi-turn preset enables f_c to be tuned exactly to the transmitter frequency. Frequency f_c is determined by

$$f_c = 1/3.7R_4C_2,$$

where R_4 is in kΩ and C_2 in μF.

The overall gain may be controlled by replacing R_3 by a multiturn preset of 100 kΩ. It may also be worthwhile to experiment with the value of C_1 to obtain optimum r.f. sensitivity.

The PLL FM receiver is also best built on a small sheet of stripboard. Since the received frequencies are higher than in the case of the AM receiver, a good layout is of prime importance. Neat wiring with as few crossings as possible results in good quality and reliability. If you replace R_4 by a preset to be able to tune the receiver, you will find an oscilloscope or frequency meter of great value.

Test and usage

The receiver can be tested only with an incoming FM signal, since in view of the high frequency of the carrier, 'audible' tuning is not possible. However, provided the PLL oscillates at the correct frequency and the circuit has been built with care and attention, the receiver should work fine.

Bring the general-purpose transmitter module described in Section 3.14 (Figure 3-42), close to the photo transistor in the receiver. Connect an audio signal source providing a well-defined signal (such as that from one of your favourite CDs) to the input of the transmitter module. Tune the receiver to the centre of the channel so that the audio reproduction from the loudspeaker is optimum. The receiver so tuned may be used to tune the laser transmitter. For this purpose, connect a potentiometer of about 10 kΩ across the inputs of the transmitter.

Simple switching receivers

The receivers described earlier in this section are rather too elaborate for use as a simple switch. For that purpose, a much simpler design as shown in Figures 3-40 and 3-41 will suffice.

The circuit in Figure 3-40 is a darkness-operated switch that uses an infra-red photo transistor as detector, T_1. As its name implies, the circuit is actuated when no light falls on to T_1. When that is so, transistor T_3 is on, so that relay Re_1 is energized.

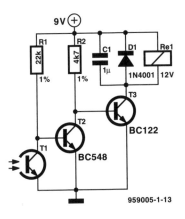

*Figure 3-40
Circuit diagram of
darkness-operated
switch*

Components list
for Figure 3-40 R_1 = 22 kΩ
R_2 = 4.7 kΩ, 1%, metal film

C_1 = 1 μF, electrolytic

D_1 = 1N4001
T_1 = infra-red photo transistor
T_2 = general-purpose n-p-n transistor, e.g., BC548
T_3 = low-power n-p-n transistor, e.g., BC122

The circuit may prove useful in a number of projects described in this book. It is, in fact, a standard circuit about which not much more can be said. Mind, however, to connect a freewheeling diode, D_1, and a small capacitor across the relay.

The opposite of the darkness switch is, of course, a light-switch, the diagram of which is shown in Figure 3-41. In this, the relay is energized when light does fall on to the photo transistor. In darkness, it is inactive.

Figure 3-41
Circuit diagram of
light-operated switch

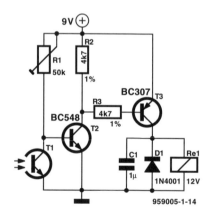

Components list
for Figure 3-41 R_1 = 50 kΩ multiturn preset potentiometer
R_2, R_3 = 4.7 kΩ, 1%, metal film

C_1 = 1 μF, electrolytic

D_1 = 1N4001
T_1 = infra-red photo transistor
T_2 = general-purpose n-p-n type, e.g., BC548
T_3 = low-power p-n-p type, e.g., BC307

Re_1 = small-signal relay, 12 V, $\leq$ 50 mA

Several types of photo transistor or diode may be used, dependent on the wavelength of the relevant transmitter—see table below.

Photo transistors

| BPW40 | collector current (in light): 6 mA
angle of incidence: 40°
central wavelength: 560 nm |
| LPT85A | photo current: 900 μA
central wavelength: 850 nm |

Photo diodes

| SFH205 | very sensitive with daylight filter
reaction time about 5 ns
central wavelength: 850 nm |
| BPW34 | sensitivity: 70 μA/lux
central wavelength: 850 nm |

Both circuits are powered by a single (assymetric) 9-V supply, which, since they both draw a very small current (except for the relay current, of course), may be a battery or a mains adaptor suitably regulated. If, instead of an electro-mechanical relay, a solid-state relay is used, appreciable powers can be switched safely, since in such relays the control input is electrically isolated from the power switch by a photoisolator.

3.14 General-purpose transmitter modules

The transmitter modules described in this section are intended primarily, but not exclusively, for use with the receivers described in Section 3.13. The first is a test transmitter whose circuit diagram is given in Figure 3-42. It is based on a virtually indestructible incoherent-light-emitting diode (LED). The use of this prevents damage to or destruction of expensive laser diodes during experimentation. The range of the test transmitter is small, but for test purposes that is not important.

Figure 3-42
Circuit diagram of
FM test transmitter

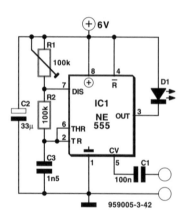

Components list for
Figure 3-42

R_1 = 100 kΩ multiturn preset potentiometer
R_2 = 10 kΩ, 1%, metal film

C_1 = 0.001 μF, ceramic
C_2 = 33 μF, 10 V, electrolytic
C_3 = 0.0015 μF, metallized polyester (MKT)

D_1 = infra-red LED or infra-red laser diode

IC_1 = NE555

The transmitter is constructed as a frequency-modulated (FM) module with variable carrier frequency, which makes it suitable for testing the FM receiver described in Section 3.13.

The output of the oscillator, IC_1, is modulated via the control voltage input (pin 5) by the output of a function generator that can generate a sine wave or a rectangular wave.

The transmitter needs a supply of 4.5–6 V, which in this case must be provided by a regulated mains-operated unit.

The transmitter may be built on a small sheet of stripboard, which can be housed in any miniature enclosure.

For the first test, we use a cheap standard LED which is later replaced by an infra-red LED or infra-red laser diode. To check whether it operates correctly, an infra-red indicator is needed: this is available from most electronics retailers or mail order firms.

The transmitter can readily be converted for operation with a laser diode simply by replacing D_1 by the diode. The sensor integrated in the diode case is not used or connected. A 100 Ω multiturn preset potentiometer is connected in series with the diode to enable the maximum current through the diode to be limited. Various types of laser diode may be used, but the one in the prototype is an LT022, which delivers an output of 5 mW at a wavelength of 780 nm. If the diode is built in an enclosure with integrated collimator, this may serve as a heat sink to absorb the not insignificant dissipation in the diode. The collimator enables the laser beam to be neatly focused for operation over long(ish) distances.

Simple pulse-modulation transmitter

Pulse modulation with fixed carrier frequency is even easier to achieve than frequency modulation—see Figure 3-43. A separate signal generator is not required. The modulation input of IC_1 (pin 5) is earthed via capacitor C_2. Just as in Figure 3-42, the current through the laser diode is not regulated. The circuit as a whole must be supplied by a regulated power supply, though. The pulse frequency, f_p, is calculated by

$$f_p = 1.44/C_1(R_1+2R_2),$$

where the resistors are in kΩ and C_1 in μF. The drawback of this circuit is that the duty factor is always greater than 0.5. This may be remedied to some extent by connecting a diode in parallel with R_2 between pins 6 and 7 of IC_1 (cathode to pin 7). With the right value of R_2, a duty factor smaller than 0.5 is attainable.

135

If a tantalum type is used for C_1, the output frequency will be more stable, since tantalum capacitors have a smaller leakage current.

Figure 3-43
Circuit diagram of
pulse modulation
transmitter

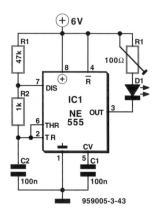

Test and usage
Test and usage are the same as described for the FM transmitter in Figure 3-42. The output frequency may be measured with an oscilloscope or a frequency meter.

Components list
for Figure 3-43

R_1 = 47 kΩ, 1%, metal film
R_2 = 1 kΩ, 1%, metal film
R_3 = 100 Ω multiturn preset potentiometer

C_1 = 0.001 µF, tantalum, bipolar
C_2, C_3 = 0.001 µF, metallized polyester (MKT)

D_1 = laser diode (Hitachi, Toshiba, Sharp, and others)

IC_1 = NE555

Wideband AM transmitter
The circuit in Figure 3-44, designed with discrete components, is eminently suitable for amplitude-modulating a transmitter diode with an analogue

136

audio signal. The circuit has current limiting to ensure stable operation of the transmitter diode. It resembles a differential amplifier with asymmetric power lines. Use is made of current feedback, which makes the operation of the transmitter diode more linear (set with R_1).

Transistor T_3, in conjunction with diodes D_1–D_3, forms a current source whose output level can be adjusted with R_4.

The value of coupling capacitor C_2 is such that the amplitude clearly increases at frequencies above 200 kHz, which gives the frequency range of the circuit an upper limit of about 5 MHz. The lower limit is around 25 Hz (with a non-linear characteristic).

Construction, test and usage

Although the circuit is a discrete design, building it is straightforward. In view of the large bandwidth of 5 MHz, construction needs to be carried out with great care and attention to detail.

To set the operating point, replace the laser diode by a resistor. Mea-

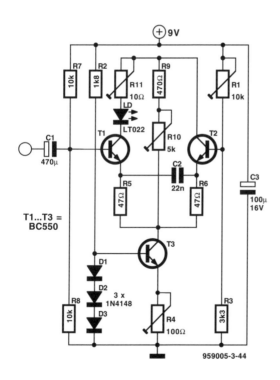

Figure 3-44
Circuit diagram of
wideband
AM transmitter

sure the potential drop across the resistor and, using Ohm's law, calculate the current. It is, of course, possible to connect an ammeter in series with the resistor to ascertain the current.

Components list for Figure 3-44

R_1 = 10 kΩ preset potentiometer
R_2 = 1.8 kΩ, 1%, metal film
R_3 = 3.3 kΩ, 1%, metal film
R_4 = 100 Ω preset potentiometer
R_5, R_6 = 47 Ω, 1%, metal film
R_7, R_8 = 10 kΩ, 1%, metal film
R_9 = 470 Ω, 1%, metal film
R_{10} = 5 kΩ preset potentiometer
R_{11} = 10 Ω multiturn preset potentiometer

C_1 = 470 μF, electrolytic
C_2 = 0.022 μF, metallized polyester (MKT)
C_3 = 100 μF, electrolytic

T_1–T_3 = BC550
D_1–D_3 = 1N4148
LD = laser diode, LT022 or equivalent

4. Simple holograms

Holography is a method of recording and reconstructing the wave front emanating from an illuminated object. Coherent light from a laser is split into two: one is a reference beam and the other illuminates the object. The waves scattered by the object and the reference beam are recombined to form an interference pattern on a photographic plate, the hologram, which records both the amplitude and phase of the scattered light. When the hologram is itself illuminated by light from a laser or other point source, two images are produced, one is virtual, but the other is real and be viewed directly. In this way, a 3-dimensional image of the object can be produced.

The basic principle of making a hologram is that by means of a beam splitter part of the coherent light from a laser is reflected towards an object and the remainder passes straight through to a photographic plate or film. The film or plate is thus illuminated by (a) light waves scattered or diffracted from the object, called the 'object beam', and (b) by a direct beam called the 'reference beam'.

The numerous points which make up the image on the film or plate are then formed by interference between the overlapping coherent waves of the object beam and the reference beam. The resulting hologram consists of a very large number of closely-spaced points, invisible to the naked eye but seen under a powerful microscope. The 'structure' of the hologram is like a diffraction grating; it has opaque and transparent regions very closely spaced.

In broadcasting, a.f. currents are arranged to modulate the carrier wave. By analogy, in making a hologram, the reference beam may be considered the 'carrier wave' which is 'modulated' at the photographic film by interference with the object beam.

After the plate is exposed and developed, the object wave, accompanied by the others due to interference, is 'recorded' on the emulsion. It may be noted that if the object moves very slightly (of the order of a fraction of a wavelength) while the photograph is taken, the diffracted waves from the object no longer produce a hologram. Rigid mounting of the object is therefore essential.

Holograms may be produced with fairly simple means, but they are, of course, not of the quality seen in commercial products. However, that is not the intention of this section anyway. But before we start on some holographic experiments, let us see what holography really is.

A hologram is a recording of interference patterns, that is, light-and-dark patterns that result when light emanated by a single coherent-light source falls on to an object and is then recorded on the emulsion of a film. All the data of the holographed object are contained in the inter-ference pattern, including those pertaining to its depth, that is, the third dimension.

A photographic plate or film so made has a very interesting prop-erty: each part of it contains all the information of the 3-D object. When a hologram is cut into two, each half contains the complete three-dimensional image, albeit that the graininess of it has increased slightly and the angle at which it may be observed is different.

The question arises: 'Where do we see the three-dimensional object with reference to the holographic plate: in front of it, in it, or behind it?' The answer is: 'Depending on the way the plate is illuminated, the image can be seen in all three positions.' Normally, when the holo-gram is illuminated with an interference beam, the object is seen be-hind the plate. For better depth, the plate must be illuminated from two sides (this is reflection holography reverted to later).

What laser output?

Because holographic film material is clearly slower than normal photo-graphic film, exposure times vary from seconds to minutes. The slightest movement or vibration of the object during the exposure ruins the recording. Because of that, it seems reasonable to use a laser with as high an output power as feasible, so that the exposure time can be kept short. And, indeed, large holograms are illuminated by a laser with an output of several watts. Considering that these are often recordings of fairly large and/or moving objects, this is the only way possible. For experimental purposes, however, a modest He-Ne laser with an output of 5–10 mW will suffice. Note that multimode lasers whose beam does not have equal properties over its cross-sectional area can not be used.

Must it be a polarized laser?

No, excellent results are also possible with non-polarized lasers, but it may happen that the resulting holograms look somewhat speckled. If high-quality holograms are required, therefore, a linearly polarized laser must be used.

Why is standard photographic film not usable?

The resolution of normal photographic films is 50–150 lines per millimetre. The higher the resolution, the lower the sensitivity and the longer the required exposure time. The reason for this is that the light-sensitive crystals in the emulsion become smaller and smaller.

A holographic film must be capable of recording interference patterns (which hold the 3-D information) whose size is comparable to the wavelength of the light used. This means that such films must often have a resolution of up to 3000 lines/mm. This also explains the long exposure times, even when a powerful laser is used. For fun, try making a hologram with standard film – the difference is astounding.

The workshop

To produce usable holograms, we need a shock and vibration proof workshop. Note that the normal optical workbench used for other laser experiments is not suitable. A hologram that is exposed for a long time may be ruined by the very small vibrations caused by passing lorry; at best, it will be unsharp and vague. So, we need a stable and vibration-proof table. Fortunately, that is made fairly easily with simple means. Compared with the optical workbench, it has the advantage that no holes need to be drilled or threads have to be tapped.

First, we have to find a quiet location. A cellar with concrete floor is excellent, while a living room with carpeted floor is a bad one. The basis for the table is formed by a sand-box, which is available as a kit from many do-it-yourself retailers. To give you enough freedom of movement, the box should not be too small: 1.5×1 metre is about the minimum, larger is better. When the box has been put together, fill it with clean, fine sand. Coarse sand, grit and gravel are definitely not suitable.

The next item you need is a 10 mm, or better 20 mm, thick sheet of hardened aluminium – the base plate – whose length and width depend on the size of the sand-box: inner dimensions of this less 20 cm. For instance, if the inside dimensions of the box are 148 × 98 cm, the base plate must measure 128 × 78 cm.

Additionally, you need four short aluminium bars with a diameter of 30–50 mm and about 50 mm long. All these dimensions are intended as guidelines only and may be deviated from within reasonable limits – this will hardly affect the holograms. The aluminium bars are fitted near the corners of the base plate to prevent this shifting in the sand-box.

Have a metal processing firm produce a number, say, 15–20. of 8 × 8 cm aluminium blocks, 2 cm thick. The large sides must be absolutely level and smooth to enable the blocks to be placed on the aluminium sheet without any wobble. Drill a 4.2 mm hole in exactly the centre of the blocks and tap an M5 thread in the hole. This enables mirror and lens holders to be fastened to the blocks.

Have the aluminium blocks and the top of the base plate anodized dark grey or preferably black. If you cannot find a firm to do this work for you, a good-quality lacquer may be used. However, anodizing is much to be preferred since it forms a denser film, lasts longer and is fairly scratch-proof.

Place the base plate, feet downward, into the sand-box. Use a spirit level to ensure that it is as horizontal as possible. Make certain that the sheet is wholly supported by the sand as this is the only guarantee that it will not shift (easily).

No daylight or artificial light should be allowed to enter the workroom during the exposure. So as to be able to see what your are doing, use a special green dark-room lamp, which is available from most photographic retailers.

Developing the films

Since holographic films are basically photographic films with a very high resolution, they can be developed, at least in theory, in the usual way. A good developer for this is Kodak D-19, which is available in powder form from most good photographic retailers. If you cannot get D-19, use another very fine grain developer.

First experiments

Before we start, remember that this is not a manual for producing high-grade professional holograms. To do that, consult one of the many books on the market. One of the best of these, if not the best, is the *Holography Primer*. This is, perhaps, not so much a reference work as a large collection of articles on holography. It does explain, however, what is possible in the field of holography. In the present section, we deal merely with the principles of the techniques to give you the means of starting in a simple manner without having to browse through a pile of specialist literature.

First, ensure that you have a reasonable stock of holographic plates or film; these may be ordered directly from the relevant manufacturers or your local photographic retailer. It may be necessary to consult the business trade. It should be stated that in a number of locations it is not easy to obtain small quantities of holographic material. Agfa does produce very good films in small format, but many retailers do not stock it.

The simplest holographic setup is shown in Figure 4-1. After the film/plate has been developed, this single-beam hologram may be viewed as a see-through hologram. This means simply that the film/plate, when developed, has to be illuminated from the back.

The object in this experiment should be small, with a smooth, non-reflective surface. Silver spoons, glittering jewelry, a television set, or a (stuffed) animal are not really suitable. Such objects are better used when some experience with holographic photography is obtained.

After the various parts, including the laser and the object to be filmed, but not the film itself, have been put in place, switch on the laser. The distance between the lens and object should be 40–60 cm (16–24 in). Both the object and the film (when in position) should be wholly in the diverging beam. Blank the laser beam with the aid of a shutter card. Switch off all lighting in the room, with the exception of the special green light. As mentioned earlier, green lamps are readily available from most photographic retailers. The light should be just sufficient to enable you to see what your are doing.

Next, put the film in a suitable holder in position with the emulsion side towards the object. A suitable holder is easily made, but may also be purchased. The angle between the film and the laser beam should be about 45° close to the object. Wait a few minutes to make certain

Figure 4-1
Setup for a single-
beam hologram

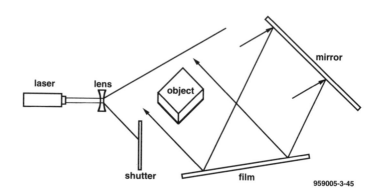

that any vibrations have died out and then quickly yet carefully remove the shutter card; after the requisite exposure time, replace the card. Do not expose the film by switching the laser on and off. This is because the coherence of the laser beam is best after th laser has been on for 20–30 minutes. The exposure time depends on the power of the laser. A good rule of thumb is 3–5 s for a power of 1 mW, 1–2 s for 3 mW and 1 s for 5 mW. It is highly recommended to use a 5 mW (He-Ne) laser: lower powers are not really suitable for holography.

It is fairly certain that the first attempts will be failures until the correct exposure time has been ascertained. The first holograms will be out of focus, under-exposed or over-exposed, or show no 3D effect. Such deficiencies are caused by vibrations or wrong exposure times. If an optical table as described earlier (see The Workshop in this chapter) is used, vibrations are highly unlikely. Difficulties with the exposure time can be eliminated with an electronic shutter.

Split-beam holograms

A serious difficulty with the setup in Figure 4-1 is the poor illumination of the object. The quality of the resulting hologram is adversely affected by dark and bright parts of the object. Just as in normal photography, better results are obtained if the object is illuminated by several sources of light. This is obvious, of course: a laser beam incident from one direction can illuminate the object only from that direction. This difficulty is solved in holography not by using several lasers, but by splitting the beam into two. A number of lenses and mirrors are used to ensure that the resulting beams illuminate the object from various directions as

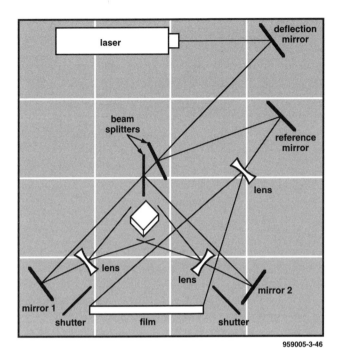

Figure 4-2
Setup for producing
split-beam holograms

shown in Figure 4-2. The resulting hologram may be viewed with the use of a broadened laser beam as the light-source.

Reflection holograms

There are various other methods of producing good-quality and easy-to-view holograms. The setup of the components needed for one of

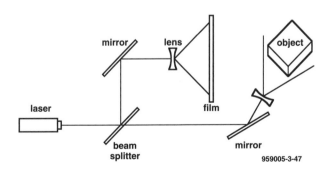

Figure 4-3
Setup for
producing
reflection
 holograms

959005-3-47

145

these on the optical table is shown in Figure 4-3. In this method, a beam splitter is also used. The reference beam illuminates one half of the holographic film/plate, while the light reflected by the object falls on to the other half. This results in a much more pronounced 3D effect, improves the general images, and enables the hologram to be viewed with the aid of a normal white source of light (such as a halogen lamp). The results of this method are very worthwhile holograms.

Double exposure results in very attractive effects. Just as in a standard double exposure, the object is turned 180° after the first exposure and then exposed again. In this way, 'moving' holograms are obtained when the hologram is viewed from different angles.

5. Glossary

Acetone
Also called propanone, CH_3COCH_3, acetone is an important organic solvent, which, in combination with lens tissue, is used for cleaning optical surfaces. It evaporates rapidly and must therefore be kept in a tightly closed bottle. Note that acetone is highly flammable.

Achromatic lens
An achromatic lens, also called antispectroscopic lens, is designed to minimize chromatic aberration. In its simplest form it consists of two component lenses, one convergent and the other divergent, made of glasses with different dispersive powers, so that different wavelengths, i.e., colours, have the same focus. See Figure 5-1.

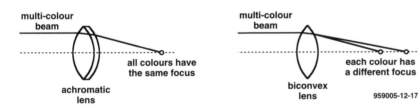

Figure 5-1
How an achromatic lens works compared with a simple lens

Acousto-optic deflector
Acousto-optic deflectors, like acousto-optic modulators, rely on the interaction between a laser beam and an effectve diffraction grating formed by an acoustic wave. As in a modulator, the grating diffracts a portion of the beam at an angle, while the rest of the beam passes straight through.

Acousto-optic modulator (AOM)
An acousto-optic modulator changes the fraction of incident light it transmits in response to external control signals. In an AOM, an acoustic wave sets up a pattern of density variations in a diffraction grating. This material diffracts part of the laser light passing through it at an angle away from the

normal beam direction.

Anode resistor

An anode resistor is required between the anode of an He-Ne laser tube and the positive high tension line. Its value is normally 35–80 kΩ. The resistor is required to stabilize the loading, since the internal resistance of the He-Ne tube varies.

AOM

See Acousto-optic modulator

Aperturing

Aperturing is a process in which the outer parts of a laser beam are blocked to remove stray light scatted by dust and lens imperfections. It is effected by spatial filters, that is, holes shaped to block unwanted portions of the beam, and serves to reduce the effect of lens aberration and to improve the beam quality.

Apodizing filter

An apodizing filter, also called graded filter, is sometimes used for aperturing. In such a filter the optical density increases away from the optical axis. The filter does not abruptly cut off the beam at a particular diameter, but gradually reduces the power density.

Argon laser

The argon laser is one of a family of ion lasers in which the active medium is an ionized rare gas. Argon, with strong lines in the blue-green and weaker lines in the ultra-violet and near-infra-red is the most important commercial type. Its prime attraction is is its ability to prodce a continuous-wave (cw) output of a few milliwatts.

Avalanche effect

The avalanche effect is the cumulative ionization that occurs when a single particle or photon ionizes several gas molecules. Each electronc and ion formed is acclerated in a strong electric field and gains sufficient energy to ionize other molecules and produce more electroncs and ions. These in turn cause further ionization and the initial event leads to a large shower of charged particles.

Beam deflector
Beam deflectors, also called scanners, are needed when a laser beam must be moved or scanned across a surface, such as in printing and the reading of bar codes. Solid-state and mechanical types are available. Solid-state scanners include acousto-optic and electro-optic types. Mechanical types include rotating mirrors and resonant mirror scanners.

Beam quality
Beam quality, that is, the geometric properties of the beam diameter and beam divergence of lasers, is normally more important than mode structure.

Beam splitter
A beam splitter is used to divide an incident beam into two parts, one of which is transmitted and the other reflected. It is typically placed at an angle of 45° to the incident beam, so that reflected light is deflected at right angles while the transmitted light passes straight through. There are several forms of beam splitter, such as partly tranparent metal films, partially silvered mirrors, specially designed prisms, types that reflect one linear polarization and transmit the orthogonal polarization, and multilayer interference coatings that selectively transmit and reflect certain wavelengths.

Beam switching
Synonymous with beam deflection or scanning.

Binary optics
Binary optics are diffractive optical elements whoe diffractive power derives from microscopic patterns on a surface.

Blanking
Blanking, that is, the shutting off or complete suppression of a laser beam, is normally effected by a solid-state modulator, but mechanical shutters are also used.

Brewster angle
The Brewster angle is synonymous with the polarizing angle. When light strikes a glass surface at an angle of incidence given by $\tan^{-1}(n)$, where n

is the refractive index, the reflected light is plane-polarized. At this angle of indicdence, the refracted ray makes an angle of 90° with the reflected ray.

Brewster window
A Brewster window is normally the terminating piece in a polarized laser tube. The ensuing polarization results from the Brewster effect which occurs at certain indices of refraction. When non-polarized light strikes a sheet of glass at the Brewster angle, the reflected lights consists solely of polarized photons. In a laser tube, these photons produce an avalanche effect, whereby more and more polarized photons are released. Other directions of polarization are not reflected. See Figure 5-2.

Figure 5-2
Brewster window

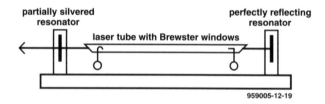

Cavity dumping
Cavity dumpig is used to couple laser energy directly out of the laser oscillator cavity without having it pass through an output mirror. Both cavity mirrors are then totally reflective and sustain a high circulating power within the laser cavity. This power can be dumped out of the cavity by deflecting it.

Chirping
Direct modulation of narrow-line semiconductor lasers causes additional broadening of their wavelength range because variations in electron density change the refractive index of the semiconductor. This changes the effective length of the laser cavity and thus the resonant wavelength, which then shifts, or chirps, during a pulse.

Cladding
The clear dielectric material of lower refractive index enclosing the core of an optical fibre.

Coatings
Coatings are materials applied to optical substrates to provide filter action.

Coherence
If waves are in phase both in time and in space, they are said to be coherent. Sources that produce coherent light are necessary to observable interference effects. A laser is a source of coherent light.

Collimator
A device or system that produces a beam of (near) parallel light. One type consists of a light source at the principal focus of a convex lens or mirror. A collimeter with very short focal length is needed with laser diodes to convert the strongly divergent beam into a parallel one. The focal length is of the order of millimetres. Since with such a short focal length serious image errors may occur, the collimator is usually a combination of lenses instead of a single lens—see Figure 5-3.
A collimator with three lenses as shown produces very good beam qual-

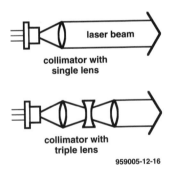

collimator with
single lens

collimator with
triple lens

959005-12-16

laser beam

*Figure 5-3
Diagram of a single-lens collimator and one composed of three lenses*

ity, but the power losses may be as much as 25%. This means that a 5 mW laser has an effective output power of only 3 mW. In optical fibre systems, collimators are used to couple a laser beam with a diameter of only a few millimetres into a fibre with a diameter of only a few micrometres. In this case, the collimator lenses must meet stringent specifications, particularly when different wavelengths are used which in case of a single lens would have different foci. In such cases, achromatic collimator lenses are used.

Coupler
A device used for combining a lasr and an optical fibre or two optical fibre cables.

Cylindrical lens
A cylindrical lens is one of which one or both faces are shaped like a portion of the curved surface of a cylinder.

Dichroic filter
A dichroic filter is a beam-splitting mirror whose wavelength depends on the coating. There are reflective and transmissive types. The latter include those for the colours red, green, and blue, while the former embrace those for the complementary colours yellow, cyuan and magenta. If only complementary filters are used, three suffice to produce the seven colours of the rainbow by subtractive colour blending. The coating is normally applied to one side of a sheet of heat-resistant glass, while the other side is not coated. These filters are anything but narrowband, so that the transmitted or reflected colours will contain tiny portions of unwanted lines or colours.

Diffraction
Diffraction is another name for scattering.

Figure 5.4
Basic patterns of
different types of
diffraction grating

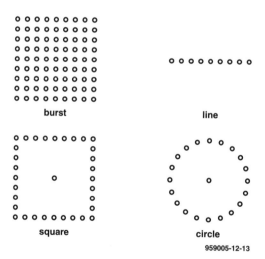

959005-12-13

Diffraction grating

A diffraction grating is a very useful optical device for producing spectra by diffraction and for the measurement of wavelength. Typically, it consists of a large number of equidistant parallel straight lines (6000–10 000 per cm) ruled on on a sheet of glass with a diamond point. Diffracted light from a narrow source produces maxima of spectral lines. There are various models available with basic patterns as shown in Figure 5-4.

Dispersion

The variation of the refractive index of a material with the wavelength (colour) of the light output of a laser or optical fibre.

Dynamic range

The full range of signal levels, or power outputs, contained in a signal or laser output, normally expressed in decibels.$\Delta 157$

Electro-optic modulator

Electro-optic modulators are used for moving a beam or causing it to scan a surface. They act in a similar way as acousto-optic modulators, and offer better resolutions than these. They are, however, much more expensive.

Energy levels

According to quantum theory, the energy of an atom, that is, the energy due to motion and electrostatic interactions of the nucleus and electrons, can have only certain fixed values and only change value by an integral multiple of some fixed amount. These allowed states of an atom are called energy levels.

Excitation

Excitation is the energy required to raise an atom above its ground state. An atom so raised is said to be in an excited state.

Fibre optics

Fibre optics is the technology of optical systems that use a single glass fibre or an array of fibres as a means of transmitting light images.

Focal length

The focal length of a lens is the distance, measured along the principal axis, between the principal focus and the second principal point.

Frequency and photon energy
Frequency and photon energy are equivalent measurements. This follows from the Planck relationship $E = hv$, where E is energy, h is the Planck constant, and v is the frequency.

Frequency doubler
A frequency doubler is a crystal with an anti-reflection coating which halves the wavelength, that is, doubles the frequency, of incident laser light. For instance, it converts the light of an Nd:YAG laser with a wavelength of 1064 nm into green light of 532 nm.

Fully silvered mirror
A fully silvered mirror is one that provides perfect reflection of incident light.

Grating spectrum
A grating spectrum is one produced by a diffraction grating.

Ground state
The ground state of a system is that in which it is in its lowest energy level, that is, when it is not excited. Also called normal state.

Helium-neon (He-Ne) laser
A helium-neon laser uses a mixture of helium and neon and is excited electrically. Its output is in the visible region at 632.8 nm.

Holographic film
Holographic film is film that has a much greater resolution than standard photographic film: 3000 lines mm^{-1} as compared with 50–150 lines mm^{-1}.

Holography
Holography was invented by Dennis Gabor (1900–1979), an Anglo-Hungarian physicist and Professor of Applied Electron Physics at Imperial College, London. It is interesting to note that Gabor produced his first holograms in 1948, more than a decade before lasers were introduced. In

1971 he received the Nobel Prize for Physics for his work on holography.

When an object is photographed by a camera, only the intensity of the light from its different points is recorded on the photographic film to form the image. Now, the intensity is a measure of the mean square value of the amplitude of the original light waves from the object. Consequently, the phase of the wave arriving at the film from the different points on the object is lost.

In holography, however, both the phase and amplitude of the light waves are recorded on the film. The resulting photograph is called a hologram. It is a speckled pattern of fine dots. Dr Gabor arrived at this name from the Greek 'holos' meaning 'the whole', because it contains the whole information about the light wave, that is, its phase as well as its amplitude.

Gabor's method of producing a hologram and of reconstructing the original wave were difficult in the 1940s, because then only sources that remain coherent over very short paths were available. In 1962, however, the laser was invented. This gave a powerful source of light that remained coherent over long paths and the subject of holography then developed rapidly.

Integrated Services Digital Network (ISDN)
ISDN is a set of telecommunication servicesd based on a digital version of the existing telephone networks. Instead of analogue signals, which have been used ever since the invention of the telephone, the ISDN uses digital datastreams which may, in principle, be conveyed via available PSTN (Public Switched Telephone network) links.

Interference
Interference is interaction between several waves of the same frequency originating from coherent sources of light.

Interference disc
Interference disks produces attractive 'smear' effects on a projection screen. Transmission time variations and superimposition of laser light result in 'cloud' effects which can be accentuated by the use of a multicolour laser and a prism.

Krypton laser
A laser that uses krypton, an ionized inert gas. It is capable of producing a

continuous wave (CW) output in the visible and the ultraviolet regions, but is used primarily for generating red light. The characteristics of a krypton laser are comparable to those of an argon laser.

Laser head

A laser head consists of a laser tube housed in a normally cylindrical metal enclosure and provided with an anode resistor an a connector. This construction is much more robust than a laser tube.

Laser pen

A laser pen is a laser pointer constructed in the shape of a ballpen.

Laser physics

The formal name for laser physics is quantum electronics, a name that dates back to the early days of laser research. Today, quantum electronics is used mainly in connection with academic research.

Laser pointer

A laser pointer is a small semiconductor laser mounted in a slender, light and easy-to-hold case. It is powered by a battery and produces a tiny, bright dot of light. Its output is restricted to 1 mW by law.

LED

See light-emitting diode

Lens tissue

Lens tissue is a very fine, extremely smooth paper that does not lose its fibres. It is highly hygroscopic. It is ideal for cleaning lenses and other optical surfaces since it does not (when used normally) scratch the surface.

Light-emitting diode

A light-emitting diode, commonly abbreviated to LED, is made from semiconductor material that, when an electric current is passed through it, releases energy as light in the visible region.

Line

A line is a commonly used name in image technology for a single wavelength, or very narrow band of wavelengths, of light.

Line filter
A line filter transmits a single wavelength, or very narrow range of wavelengths, of light.

Line-rejection filter
A line rejection filter rejects a single wavelength, or very narrow range of wavelengths, of light.

Linewidth
The linewidth of laser light is its (very) narrow range of wavelengths.

Mixed-gas laser
The mixed-gas laser uses a mixture of argon and krypton. The argon makes it a much more efficient unit than a pure-krypton laser. The emitted light is spread over the entire visible region of 454–676 nm. It is this aspect that makes the mixed-gas laser a favourite for shows.

Mode diaphragm
For scientific purposes, where power is of secondary importance, a mode diaphragm, also called ring diaphragm, with very precise setting of the effective aperture, is often built into the resonator. Shutting the diaphragm enables the suppression of undesired high resonance modes. This is effected without power loss, since no part of the laser beam is suppressed.

Mode-locking
Mode locking is a technique for producing laser pulses of very short duration.

Modes
There are two types of mode in a laser resonator: longitudinal and transverse. Longitudinal modes correspond to the various resonances along the length of the laser cavity, while transverse modes manifest themselves in the in the cross-sectional profile of the beam of light, that is, in its intensity pattern.

Modulator
A modulator changes the fraction of incident light it transmits in response to external control signals.

Optical amplifier

An optical amplifier, also called laser amplifier, increases the strength of weak optical signals, usually in an optical fibre system. Such an amplifier can extend the transmission distance or increase input to a receiver. There are two types: semiconductor laser amplifier and optical-fibre amplifier.

Output power

The output power of a laser is measured in watts and multiples and sub-multiples thereof.

Photodiode

A photodiode is a semiconductor diode which has a tiny lens through which light can be focused on to the p-n junction. When light falls on to the lens, a substantial photocurrent is produced.

Photo transistor

A phototransistor is a photodetector that is operated with the base floating. When the base is subjected to electromagnetic radiation (light), a base current is produced. The light is normally incident on to the base via a tiny lens as in the photodiode.

Photon

A photon is a discrete, indivisible amount (quantum) of visible light or other electromagnetic radiation.

Polarization

Polarization is the manner in which the electric and magnetic fields of an electromagnetic wave are positioned relative to one another in a non-random way.

Polarizing filter

A polarizing filter only allows the passage of light that is polarized in one direction. It is usually made by depositing a special coating on to a sub-strate of glass or polymer.

Polarizing splitter

Strictly speaking, a polarizing splitter is a beam splitter. When a non-polarized laser beam strikes the splitter, two discrete beams are produced whose

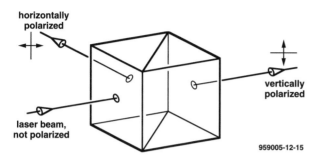

Figure 5-5
Operation of a
polarizing
splitter

planes of polarization are displaced by 90° (see Figure 5-5). Since the plane of polarization of a laser is not steady, the power of the two beams can vary. Te splitter may also be used to combine two polarized beams.

Population inversion

A population inversion is a condition in a system that is not in equilibrium in which the number of particles in the higher energy level is greater than that in the lower energy level.

Prism

A prism is an optical component that has two basic functions. The first is to split a beam of light into its constituent lines (wavelengths = colours). The second is to mirror a beam or graphic figure. When an incident beam is split, the emerging beam is a divergent one consisting of all the colours present in the original beam (see Figure 5-6). This enables the power of each discrete line to be measured, so that the power distribution of the laser can be ascertained. A standard prism has an apex angle of 90°, but there are types with different angles.

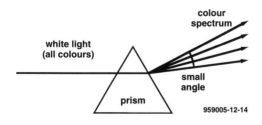

Figure 5-6
Action of a prism and
the resulting colour
spectrum

Prismatic spectrum
A prismatic spectrum is one formed by refraction in a prism (see Figure 5-6).

Pulse length
Pulse length is the same as pulse width and is the time interval between the rise time and the decay time of the pulse.

Pulse shortening
Pulse shortening is reducing the width of a pulse. It is usually effected with the aid of a pulse shaper.

Optical pumping
Optical pumping is the process in which an external light source is used to raise a species from a lower energy level to a higher one and so produce a population inversion – a prerequisite for laser action.

Q switching
Q switching is a method by which a laser can produce high instantaneous power.

Reflection
Reflection is the change in direction of a light, sound or radio wave when it strikes a certain surface and is bounced back.

Refraction
Refraction is a change in direction which occurs when a light wave enters a medium from another and the two have a different refractive index. The change is determined by Snell's law.

Refractive index
The ratio of speed of light in a transparent medium compared to the speed of light in free space.

Resonant scanner
The construction of a resonant scanner, aso called resonant-mirror scanner, is comparable to that of a beam splitter. The scanner has an integral resonant circuit that consists of an electronic part and a spring mechanism

that provides the counteraction. The circuit generates a resonance that causes a mirror to move to and fro.

Resonator
A resonator is the optical cavity in a laser that concentrates the light.

Resonator mirror
A laser needs two resonator mirrors for its action. These mirrors are fitted at either end of the laser medium (gas or solid). If stimulated emission occurs on the axis between the two mirrors, it is reflected back and forth through the medium, stimulating emission again and again. The positioning of the mirrors is of crucial importance. Since one of them is slightly concave, and thus has a certain focal length, the resonators must be exactly parallel. Ideally, the back mirror should provide total reflection, but in practice that is not possible. A good mirror provides 99.9% reflction

Safety glasses
Safety glasses, also called goggles, should be worn at all times when working with lasers. Filters in the glasses block light at the wavelength of the laser, but transmit enough other light to enable the operator to work by. It follows that there are different goggles for each type of laser.

Shift
A shift is a change in wavelength of light.

Shutter
A shutter is a device to block the output beam of a laser in certain circumstances. Its provision on most lasers is a standard safety regulation.

Snell's law
Snell's law, formulated by the Dutch physicist Snellius, relates the angles of incidence and refraction when a light wave enters a medium from another and the two have a different refractive index.

Speckle
A phenomenon whereby a speckle pattern results from the scattering of laser light by a diffusing surface.

Spectral filter
A spectral filter is one that selectively transmits and/or reflects certain wavelengths of light.

Spontaneous emission
Spontaneous emission is a process whereby energy is emitted in a laser without external excitation.

Standard mirror
A standard mirror is flat or spherical. Spherical mirrors are either concave or convex. See Figure 5-7.

Stimulated emission
Stimuated emission is the process by which an incident photon excites an atom to emit a photon. The atom is then left in the lower energy state.

Substrate
A substrate is the base material of a semiconductor with a controlled impurity level on to which one or more layers are deposited.

Surface mirror
A surface mirror is one that is highly reflective. Normally, glass is used as carrier (substrate) for the reflective coating, since it has a very precise surface smoothness, is inexpensive, and is not heavy. The coating is on the glass, not behind it as with domestic mirrors (see Figure 5-7). The coating may consist of aluminium which is protected by a very thin layer of quartz. This type of mirror is suitable for low-power lasers only. For higher powers, it is better to use a dielectric mirror, in which the reflectivity is enhanced by the application of a transparent dielectric material.

Tectonics
The study of the major structural features of the earth's crust.

Transition
In laser technology, a transition is a change from one energy level to another.

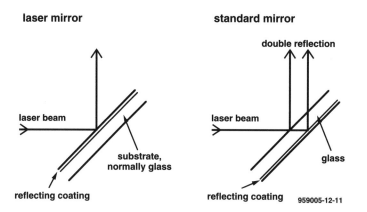

laser mirror

laser beam

substrate,
normally glass

reflecting coating

standard mirror

double reflection

laser beam

glass

reflecting coating   959005-12-11

Figure 5-7
The construction of a standard mirror is fundamentally different from that of a laser mirror

Tuning

Tuning is adjusting the laser wavelength, which is usually done with a prism or grating inserted into the optical cavity.

Wavelength

The wavelength of a light-wave is the distance between two successive points at which the wave has the same phase. In laser technology, it is usually measured in nanometres ($nm = 10^{-9}$ m).

Index

CL